RIGS AND RIGGING OF YACHTS

RIGS AND RIGGING
OF YACHTS

by

D. PHILLIPS-BIRT, A.M.I.N.A.

The art of masts, sail crowded, fit to break,
yet stayed to strength. MASEFIELD

ADLARD COLES LTD.
IN ASSOCIATION WITH
GEORGE G. Harrap & CO. LTD.
LONDON · TORONTO · WELLINGTON · SYDNEY
AND JOHN DE GRAFF INC. NEW YORK

By the same author

SAILING YACHT DESIGN
MOTOR YACHT AND BOAT DESIGN

Dedicated to

ELSPETH AND GERVAS HUXLEY

First Published 1954

*Copyright in all countries signatory
to the Berne Convention*

COMPOSED IN 11 ON 12 BASKERVILLE AND
MADE AND PRINTED IN GREAT BRITAIN
BY W. & J. MACKAY & CO. LTD., CHATHAM

CONTENTS

LIST OF PLATES

LIST OF DIAGRAMS

SAIL PLANS

ACKNOWLEDGEMENTS

It is with pleasure that I acknowledge my debt to Mr. Frank Hall, whose patient and skilful photography produced most of the illustrations in this book. He not only took the photographs, but spent many hours of his leisure developing and enlarging them, and his insistence on obtaining the best results was of the greatest value to me.

Mr. Maurice Griffiths was kind enough to write the account, which appears on page 62, of his experience in designing and handling General Sir Frederick Browning's wishbone ketch *Jean d'Arc*. Mr. Humphrey Barton read many of my chapters, and kindly devoted time to making extensive notes based on his probably unrivalled experience of handling rigging at sea. Colonel H. G. Hasler provided full notes and numerous sketches of the Vosper–Hasler Lapwing rig, and these were a model of clarity. Mr. George Gill read and commented on Chapter 3, which I think has his general agreement.

The *Yachting Monthly* has allowed me to reproduce in the text material which originally appeared in their pages, and to this journal and its unfailingly helpful Editor I am grateful. I owe thanks for the same reason to Mr. A. H. Smart and The Yachting Press Ltd. Messrs. Camper and Nicholsons allowed me the use of photographs of their halyard and sheet winches, and Messrs. Laurent Giles and Partners provided *Figs. 17* and *26*. Messrs. Wrights Ropes Ltd. examined and made a number of suggestions for Chapter 6, and Messrs. Beken supplied Plates 1, 11 and 59. Mr. Morris Rosenfeld supplied Plates 5, 12, 58, 60 and 61, Mr. F. G. Warne Plate 10, Mr. Graham Gullick Plate 13.

I am also greatly indebted to Group Captain E. F. Haylock, R.A.F., Retd., Editor of the *Yachting World*, for permission to reproduce a selection of sail plans from the monthly Design Supplements of the periodical. The uniform style of the tracings, scaled and giving sail areas and rigging schedules make these most valuable for reference and comparison.

Peggy as usual typed, corrected, and revised, and where necessary made sense out of nonsense, with the same accuracy as she often displays when identifying a strange landfall.

PLATES

PLATE 2 The gaff rig in its most modern form, with what is virtually a Bermudian mainsail split by a gaff.

PLATE 3 The rod rigging of a 5.5-Metre. From this angle kinks in the rod will be apparent; but only excessive tension, encouraging failure in the rods or terminal fittings, will draw out such kinks, and they are not of importance. The tubular spreaders will also be noticed.

PLATE 5 *Wind Call*, a true masthead sloop by Sparkman and Stephens. The single forestay is from the masthead to the stemhead, and there is no inner forestay. Runners are eliminated. The mast is of light alloy only slightly tapered, and the shroud plan is very simple, with a single set of spreaders. The simplification of the staying is assisted by the relatively big beam of the boat.

PLATE 4 A scarph on the fore-side of a hollow, spruce mast. Below this the longitudinal joints between the pieces of spruce forming the mast may also be seen. The joints are clearly visible because the glue used is a phenolic resin, which is dark in colour.

PLATE 6 A heavy type of snatch block, without spring action or snap shackle.

PLATE 7 A mainsheet buffer, suitable for large craft and heavy mainbooms. The mainsheet deck block in the foreground is prevented from twisting in the eyebolt or making contact with the deck by the cage round the eyebolt.

PLATE 8 The mainsheet rig in a 16-tonner, with the boom block riding on a wire span. Forward of this, on the underside of the boom, will be seen the after block of the topping lift purchase, sliding on a length of track which prevents the block from sagging below the boom and fouling.

PLATE 9 Snap shackle snatch blocks, which are particularly useful headsail sheet leads.

PLATE 10 Spreader attachment and tang for the intermediate shroud, in light alloy, designed by Laurent Giles for 6-Metre masts.

17

PLATE 11 *Ithuriel*, a sloop by Robert Clark, having an idle inner forestay (visible below foot of genoa) which is the substitute for the two forward lower shrouds.

PLATE 12 *Malabar VIII* with her mizzen staysail set. It is a very long-footed sail tacked down abreast of the mainmast. Forward the staysail is boomed.

PLATE 14 A masthead ketch rig with the masts, unlike *Iska*'s (Fig. 26) tied together by a spring stay. This is *Fidalga III* by John I. Thornycroft & Co., Ltd.

PLATE 13 *Jean d'Arc*, the 13-ton wishbone ketch designed by Maurice Griffiths for General Sir Frederick Browning.

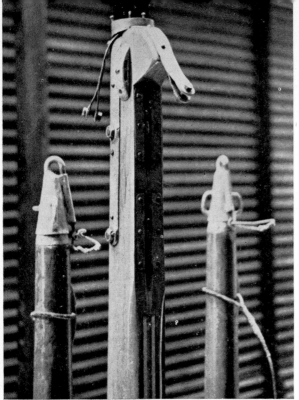

PLATE 15 Masthead and spinnaker pole fittings. The masthead carries two sheaves, the lower for the main halyard, the upper for the topping lift.

PLATE 17 The foredeck of a Clark-designed ocean racer. Double forestays are fitted, set up by two levers on the centreline. Winches for the tack pendants are on either side of these.

PLATE 16 An arrangement at the masthead having topmast forestay and backstay spliced over the masthead. The latter passes over a backstay chock, to which it is not very adequately secured. The topmast shrouds are hung on a bolt which is not a strong arrangement, though neat and light. The sheave, correctly, has sufficient diameter to give the main halyard a fair lead into, and out of, the mast mortise.

PLATE 18 A single-ended mainsheet led along the boom and down into the boat amidships, where the winch and cleat are fitted on a sampson post in the middle of the cockpit. This arrangement is suitable for half-decked racing craft, and is seen here in a 5.5-Metre. It may be compared with the mainsheet lead, in a boat of the same class, in Plate 19.

PLATE 19 A double-ended mainsheet giving a power of four. The narrow mainsheet horse will be noticed. The blocks are of Tufnol.

PLATE 20 Rigging screws encased in metal tubes packed with grease. Wooden anti-chafe rollers will be seen on the intermediate and upper shrouds.

PLATE 21 A mainsheet in a large schooner, giving a power of six.

PLATE 22 An orthodox rig of double sheet for a headsail. There is a bullseye spliced into the end of the wire clew pendant, and the hemp sheet is rove through this, and through the two fixed deck bonnets. Note the stopper knot in the forward bonnet.

PLATE 23 A light alloy sheet winch with the handle under the side deck. Also a tee-section deck track with a metal bonnet lined with lignum vitae. This has a screw adjustment on the track.

PLATE 24 A single part headsail sheet lead. This bonnet is on the track used in combination with the smaller headsails, and its angle to the centreline will be observed. The genoa sheet deck track may be seen abaft this and as close to the edge of the deck as possible. On the port side, aft, may be seen the flat, open-ended deck block of the runner.

PLATE 25 A channel-section deck track with a Tufnol block in the slide. The winch has its handle under the deck.

PLATE 26 Adjustable headsail sheet bonnets on a tee-section track fastened on top of the rail, and hence as far outboard as possible. The eyeplate fitting abaft the bonnets is designed to carry a block, preferably a snap shackle snatch block (Plate 9), for a block, unlike a bonnet, allows the sheet to be led forward again if necessary to a winch. A block, rather than a bonnet, is desirable where the lead of a sheet departs far from a straight line. A wood knee stiffening the rail in way of the track will be seen on the extreme left.

PLATE 27 The sheeting arrangement of a boomed staysail. The upper sheet block in this case rides on a saddle shackle on a wire span.

PLATE 28 A staysail boom gooseneck pivoted on the barrel of the forestay's rigging screw. The track on the boom for the staysail foot may be seen, a refinement of doubtful value enforcing a headsail trimmed with excessive flatness, and aggravating the inevitable weakness of a boomed headsail.

PLATE 29 Internal wire halyards with rope tails lead from the heel of a light alloy mast. On the port side is the main halyard, set up on the winch. On the starboard side the headsail halyard is belayed by hooking it on to the hook plate to starboard of the winch, and the halyard is set up by the lever beside the mast, which hardens the tack pendant.

PLATE 30 A mainsheet of power in a ketch. The simple lanyard type of main clew outhaul will be seen.

PLATE 31 A type of clew outhaul, which may be compared with that in Plate 32. The wire pendant here passes over the groove at the forward end of the outhaul—an arrangement which obviates the possibility of the failure of the sheave pin in Plate 32. The arrangement is otherwise similar. The eyebolts carrying the mainsheet blocks hold the blocks to the centreline of the boom, and hence introduce twisting stresses in it, which are carried by the gooseneck unless this is of the swivelling type.

PLATE 32 Another type of main clew outhaul, working on a heavy tee-section track. The purchase is on the port side of the boom, the wire pendant being led over a side sheave (Plate 33) at the end of the boom. The twisted shackle, with its pin in an athwartship plane to take the clew cringle, will be noted; also the hoop attachment of the treble block of the mainsheet, which relieves the boom of twisting stresses.

PLATE 33 A boom showing a channel-section track for the foot of the mainsail, and a heavy tee-section track for the clew outhaul slide. The sheave at the end of the boom on the port side is for the outhaul pendant. See also Plate 32.

PLATE 34 The arrangement which has now been generally replaced by metal tangs—hardwood bolsters at the hounds to support the eyesplices of the shrouds.

PLATE 35 An older pattern of mastband tang with lightening holes, and made in two halves bolted round the mast. Single lugs welded to the band carry the shrouds, which must therefore be secured with shackles. A single lug hung on the bolt passing through the flanges of a mastband carries the forestay.

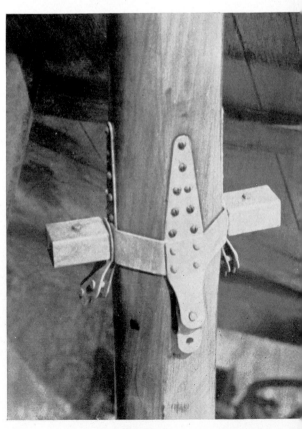

PLATE 36 A mastband carrying simple lugs for the lower shrouds and forestay.

PLATE 37 A spreader and tang assembly. The lower part of the forestay fork is extended to carry the headsail halyard block.

PLATE 38 A tang assembly by Laurent Giles, embodying sockets for jumper struts, forks formed by straps welded to the lower part of the tang for shrouds and forestay, and lugs to carry the halyard blocks.

PLATE 39 Strap tangs on the mast of a 40-tonner. The upper and lower part of the forks carrying the forestay and shrouds are each of two thicknesses of metal, the tangs being in effect laminated.

PLATE 40 Tang assembly and halyard sheave in light alloy designed by Laurent Giles. The tang is hung on a hollow through bolt, to the ends of which the tubular spreader is screwed, as in Plate 10.

PLATE 41 The same chainplate as illustrated in Plate 42. The load carried in the chainplate is further spread by the clamp fitted below, and hard against, the deck shelf (the member into which the deck beams are mortised).

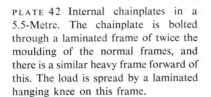

PLATE 42 Internal chainplates in a 5.5-Metre. The chainplate is bolted through a laminated frame of twice the moulding of the normal frames, and there is a similar heavy frame forward of this. The load is spread by a laminated hanging knee on this frame.

PLATE 43 Masthead ironwork. The lower part of the fork for the standing backstay is extended to carry the topping lift.

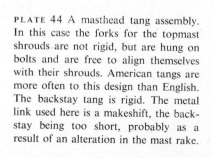

PLATE 44 A masthead tang assembly. In this case the forks for the topmast shrouds are not rigid, but are hung on bolts and are free to align themselves with their shrouds. American tangs are more often to this design than English. The backstay tang is rigid. The metal link used here is a makeshift, the backstay being too short, probably as a result of an alteration in the mast rake.

PLATE 45 Runner layout, with the runner riding on a wire span. There is no purchase in the rope tail, but if necessary one may be incorporated when there is no sheet winch; though in small craft this will not be necessary.

PLATE 46 The original type of Highfield lever, which is still extensively used. Near it is a direct action sheet winch secured to a steel bracket and not to a hardwood chock, which would break water into the cockpit. The winch has bottom handle operation, the catches for the handle being visible.

PLATE 47 A cockpit layout in a Clark-designed ocean racer. Two geared headsail sheet winches are to port and starboard. Spanning the after end of the bridge deck is the mainsheet track, giving a wide range of adjustment, and the stops to limit this range when necessary may be seen to port and starboard of the mainsheet track block. The mainsheet is double-ended, belayed on cleats on either side of the mainsheet winch.

PLATE 48 Orthodox type of top-handle lever winch suitable for all craft, by Camper and Nicholson.

PLATE 49 Forward is a two-speed genoa sheet winch suitable for yachts of about 35 ft. on the waterline. To operate in the lower gear the handle is placed over the spindle which may be seen at the base of the winch. This winch has whelps on the barrel. Aft is a less powerful geared sheet winch. The markedly different shapes of barrel will be noticed.

PLATE 50 A large barrel geared sheet winch with the handle under the deck. A wire sheet clamp is shown abaft the winch. The jaws are closed over the wire by a single movement of the handle, this enabling the sheet to be belayed without taking turns on a cleat. Both fittings are by Camper and Nicholson.

PLATE 51 A large two-geared headsail winch placed aft on the counter and able to handle port and starboard sheets. The barrel of the winch has wide flanges and is slightly radiused.

PLATE 53 A runner winch made by Camper and Nicholson for Dragon-class boats, and suitable for half-decked and semi-open craft in which under deck winching for the runners may be arranged. The wire is wound on the drum, and there is a quick release cam. The handle stows by folding over the winch.

PLATE 54 A Merriman self-stowing halyard winch also manufactured in Great Britain under licence by Francis Shaw & Co., Ltd.

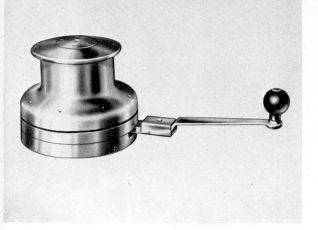

PLATE 55 The new C.R. cam-operated two-speed winch.

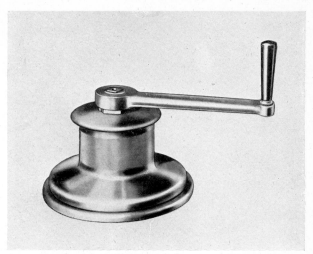

PLATE 56 A top handle model of the C.R. two-speed winch.

PLATE 57 A battery of three, self-stowing, direct-action halyard winches.

PLATE 58 The ketch *Malabar VIII* by John Alden. Here the main and mizzen are stayed together into a single unit. The mainmast carries jumper struts and stays as well as a forestay from the masthead. The mainmast has twin standing backstays, and the mizzenmast a standing backstay carried on a bumpkin. Runners are eliminated.

PLATE 59 A genoa trimmed for windward work. The 6-Metre *Titia*, designed by David Boyd and built in 1952.

PLATE 60 *Fun*, a typical American, modern sloop. It will be observed that the shroud plan is simple, consisting of one set of spreaders and one pair of widely-angled, long, jumper struts. The topping lift, with a two-part purchase above the boom, will be noticed. Also the tricing lines on the genoa.

PLATE 61 The large yawl *Bolero*, by Sparkman and Stephens. The masts have very little taper, and it will be seen that the mainmast above the forestay is unsupported by shrouds or jumper stays. Main and mizzen masts are stayed independently, the standing backstay of the mainmast having a span in its lower part, with the legs to port and starboard of the mizzen mast.

PLATE 62 A good pattern of gooseneck for large craft. Integral with the boom fitting are the metal ears carrying the bolt securing the tack of the mainsail. Mast hoops will be seen, and also the tops of self-stowing halyard winches to port and starboard on the mast.

PLATE 63 On the mast (right) the track at its lower end is carried out from the mast on a tapered batten, which gives the luff of the sail a fair lead on to the boom, making allowance for the length of the roller reefing gooseneck fitting. Without the batten the luff rope may foul the reefing mechanism as rolls are taken in the mainsail.

PLATE 64 A sliding gooseneck in a heavy track securely side-fastened to the mast. The downhaul purchase may be seen beneath the boom; also, on the port side of the mast a magazine track for the trysail, and forward of the mast a wooden anti-chafe roller on the inner forestay. No sail is set on this forestay, which is placed to restrain the tendency of the lower part of the mast from sagging aft.

PLATE 65 A worm roller reefing gear (also known as the Appledore pattern). The track is deeply recessed into the boom.

PLATE 66 The mainsheet and topping lift attachment for a roller reefing boom. The eye welded on top of the metal cap at the end of the boom is for the main clew outhaul lanyard.

PLATE 67 A piece of cloth lashed to the runner to mark the position of the runner when fully set up.

PLATE 68 An alternative and stronger mainsheet and topping lift attachment for a roller reefing boom. The fittings are on a metal band riding on a collar.

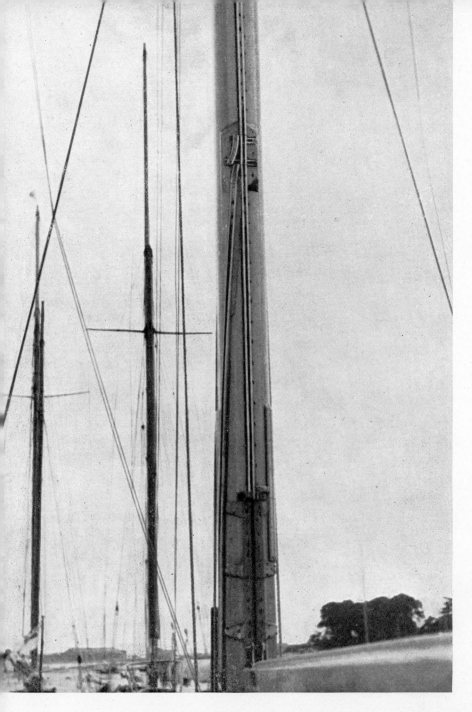

PLATE 69 A channel-section mast track with magazine track on the port side of the mast for the trysail, and a "gate" sliding horizontally for shunting trysail slides on to the main track.

THE EFFICIENCIES OF RIGS

IF yachts were aeroplanes the relative efficiencies of rigs would by now have been thrashed out mathematically and in wind tunnels; as it is the matter remains largely empirical. The most accurate data, derived from the only feasible source—experience at sea over many years—is to be found in the rig allowances embodied in the rules of the Royal Ocean Racing Club and the Cruising Club of America, which are in close agreement with one another, and which have been proved to estimate very fairly the merits of the various rigs.

The rig allowances, expressed as percentages of the square roots of the rated sail areas, are shown in the following table, the sloop and the cutter forming the basis of comparison and being rated at 100 per cent.

Rig Allowances in Percentages of Sail Area (Rated)		
	R.O.R.C.	C.C.A.
Bermudian Sloop	100	100
Bermudian Cutter	100	100
Bermudian Yawl*	98	98
Staysail Ketch (Bermudian)	—	97
Gaff Cutter	96	97
Bermudian Schooner	96	—
Staysail Schooner	—	96
Wishbone Schooner	96	—
Bermudian Ketch* & Wishbone Ketch	94	92
Gaff Yawl*	94	93
Schooner, Bermudian Main Gaff Fore	—	93
Gaff Schooner	92	90
Gaff Ketch*	90	90

The above figures may be rounded up and approximated as follows in terms of the percentage increase in sail area required by the various two-masted rigs to attain equality with a Bermudian sloop or cutter:

A Bermudian Yawl needs   4 per cent more sail area
A Gaff Cutter needs   6 per cent more sail area
A Bermudian Schooner needs 8 per cent more sail area
A Gaff Yawl needs   13 per cent more sail area
A Bermudian Ketch needs   13 per cent more sail area
A Gaff Schooner needs   18 per cent more sail area
A Gaff Ketch needs   20 per cent more sail area

* A deduction of 1 per cent measured rating is allowed under R.O.R.C. rule if no mizzen staysail is carried. For details of R.O.R.C. and C.C.A. rules see Appendix I.

It will be evident that such figures simply outline the picture, and when the details are filled in the prospect may appear very different. Thus the gulf between a ketch and a sloop may be bridged when one is efficiently and the other badly rigged.

To-day the Cruising Club of America is the premier cruising organisation of the world's greatest yachting nation, and as such its fleet of nearly 300 sailing craft form a microcosm of American types of yacht, and suggest the degree to which each rig is favoured by experienced yachtsmen. An analysis of the fleet shows that a little more than half of it consists of two-masters, the remainder being sloops and cutters. The actual ratio of the two to the single masters is 6.75 : 6.25.

The two-master part of the fleet is composed thus: Schooners 22 per cent; Ketches 30 per cent; Yawls 48 per cent. The popularity of the yawl—nearly one-quarter of the total fleet—is striking, yet perhaps not surprising, for the rig makes the nearest approach to the effectiveness of a sloop or cutter whilst offering the advantages for cruising of a divided sail plan. Perhaps it is this fact, as much as the rating benefits obtained by the rig, which accounts for its popularity. The high proportion of schooners in the fleet is un-English, but it may equally be felt that the greater popularity of ketches—30 per cent of the two-master fleet compared with 22 per cent—is un-American. The traditional two-masted American rig may be the schooner, as the ketch is that of England, but to-day the fact would seem to be that whilst the schooner is much more popular in the U.S.A. than in Britain, the ketch is more popular than the schooner in both countries. We may smile to remember that Dixon Kemp once wrote of the ketch: " A rig now seldom used except by coasters; it has all the disadvantages of the schooner or yawl rig, and none of its advantages."

Conservatism is a notable feature of the schooner fleet. Of staysail schooners, the rig which originated in the U.S.A. in 1924 when the Burgess-designed *Advance* appeared, there is only one example, the famous *Nina*, also by Burgess. When this rig was devised it seemed a great improvement upon the traditional schooner, and while engaged some years ago on an exploratory design of a yacht for the American market the staysail schooner rig was chosen without hesitation in preference to the older type. But ultimately the ketch rig was adopted, a choice which the above analysis would seem to justify. Where schooners are concerned the Cruising Club would emphatically seem to prefer the older type. About a third of the schooner fleet have both gaff mainsails and foresails; most of the others have Bermudian main and gaff foresail.

The once bitter controversy over the rival merits of the gaff and Bermudian rigs has now settled itself pretty definitely on the side of the Bermudian. The evidence of this lies in the yachtsmen's choice as revealed in the yachting fleets of recent years. The boats under construction, in commission, or on the second-hand market are mainly Bermudian rigged. Even the ocean wanderers now prefer it. Thirty years ago, after crossing the Atlantic in *Firecrest*, Alan Gerbault converted the yacht to Bermudian for his further wanderings in the Pacific. And to-day both *Beyond* and *Wanderer III*, designed specifically for such extensive voyages, have this rig; although *Wanderer*'s owner, Mr. Eric Hiscock, may not be permanently converted to it.

Yet in certain quarters the gaff rig continues to hold its own. About ten years ago more than 60 per cent of the newer boats built for members of the Royal Cruising Club were gaff rigged, and so still to-day are a surprisingly high proportion of the yachts flying this burgee. Reasons other than that of pure fitness for its work may account for the persistence of the rig. One of the strongest of these must be the bias in its favour on the part of yachtsmen who have covered many thousands of sea miles under gaff rig, who have learned to handle it to its best advantage, who understand it completely. When a man has acquired full mastery of one instrument he is wise not to change it for another. But this is also a reason why the rig is likely to become even more rare than it is to-day. And some of the most experienced members of the R.C.C., owners themselves of gaff-rigged yachts, have assured me that they would change to the Bermudian rig to-morrow if it cost nothing to do so.

What advantages may be claimed for the gaff rig? For a given sail area it may have a shorter mast. It is thus effective for the small sail plans of boats of the motor-sailer type. In short-ended craft with very full body and heavy displacement, and perhaps light

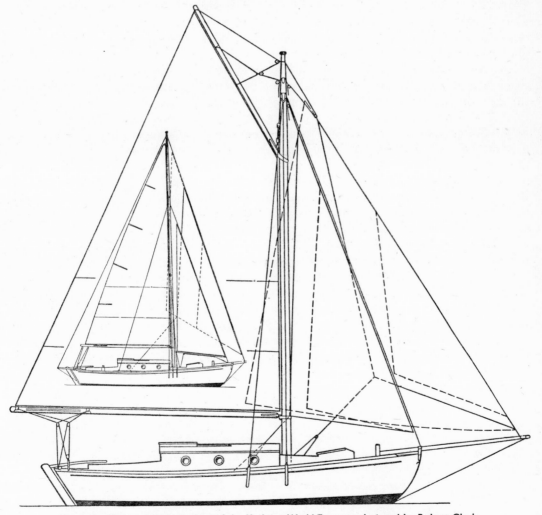

Figure 1.—Comparative sail plans of the *Yachting World* 5-tonner designed by Robert Clark.

draft also and moderate ballast ratio, it is difficult to set enough sail area in the Bermudian rig without a mast of excessive height and a sail plan having its centre of effort too high for the limited stability of the hull. Greater drive with a smaller heeling moment may be derived from the well-designed gaff rig above such a hull, at the sacrifice of a degree of windward ability which the hull will anyhow be incapable of using under most conditions. Brixham Trawlers, Bristol Channel Pilot Cutters, and yachts which have been converted from other of the heavier types of fishing vessel, do not perform well under the Bermudian rig, and the gaff is the reasonable choice.

It may also be so in large craft, especially to-day when reduced crews necessitate small individual sails. An effective use of the gaff rig is seen in *Aries*, the 125-ton ketch built by Messrs. Camper and Nicholsons in 1952–3 (Plate 2). The profile of the gaff mainsail and thimble-headed topsail is essentially that of a Bermudian mainsail, and the short gaff is chiefly a means of reducing the sail area abaft the mainmast into two more easily handled portions. A smaller mainsail has thus to be handled, and the job of reefing, which is not easy in so large a craft, may be initially avoided by handing the topsail. The price paid for the conveniences offered by the gaff are: (i) A less efficient area of canvas abaft the mast owing to the interference of the gaff with the setting of the mainsail and the topsail; (ii) the weight of the gaff when hoisting and aloft; (iii) the need for three halyards and a topsail sheet instead of the single halyard of a Bermudian mainsail.

An instructive comparison between the gaff and Bermudian cutter rigs as applied to small craft is seen in the two sail plans (*Fig.* 1) drawn by Robert Clark for the *Yachting World* 5-tonner designed by him. The maximum sail area under gaff rig is about 12 per cent more than under Bermudian, and the gaff mainsail has an area of 40 per cent more than the Bermudian sail. This concentration of area in a mainsail with its boom overhanging the transom by a couple of feet is an obvious disadvantage. At the other end of the ship a very long bowsprit is needed to spread the sail plan, and whilst the short bowsprit of the Bermudian cutter allows the jib to be hanked to the stay, in the gaff rig it has to be set flying. Both forward and aft of the mast the gaff rig is the more difficult to handle, and for windward work would be much inferior, with a less effective combination of sails in the fore-triangle, and also no runners.

The gaff cutter has the shorter mast, yet it is a less secure one, without standing backstay or runners, and with a greater unsupported length both athwartships and fore and aft. It is, in fact, not so well stayed; but this cannot be remedied within the limitations of the normal gaff rig when set above a small hull. In one respect the gaff rig does score: the simplicity of its gear and staying makes its initial cost cheaper, and possibly its upkeep also.

2

MODERN RIGS

Sloops and Cutters.—The terms sloop and cutter have always been loosely applied, and historically both terms have been used in relation to the hull and general type of a vessel as well as to the rig. In the early years of yachting sloops were craft with a standing bowsprit and the mast well forward, whilst the cutter had a running bowsprit and the mast farther aft. Gradually it came to be understood that a sloop had one headsail and a cutter two,* and this we shall accept as the difference. It should be noted however that the variety of headsails carried in many cutters enables them to sail often as sloops. *Jocasta*, a Clark-designed cutter of 26 tons, sails as a sloop, carrying her largest R.O.R.C. Genoa in winds up to Force 6, and many cutters give their best performance under single headsails. If a yacht has two forestays on which sails may be set at the same time she may be considered to be basically a cutter.

A further point of nomenclature arises. This concerns the masthead sloop—the sloop in which a headsail may be set on a forestay from the masthead. There are two types of masthead sloop: the one has a single forestay, and all the headsails are set from the masthead. The other has a lower forestay also, coming from the mast at about the same distance below the masthead as that of a normal sloop, and working headsails are set on this stay, the masthead one being used only for the larger, light weather canvas. The lower or inner forestay may be released and carried back to the mast when big headsails are set. Those two types of masthead sloop therefore differ fundamentally, and the type having two forestays on which sails may be set (though not concurrently) has been christened " slutter." This is an unattractive name which does not deserve to be perpetuated, and we shall not do so; though there is an obvious need for a name by which this increasingly popular rig may be differentiated.

Single-masted rigs are now the most popular, and for three chief reasons: (i) In the small yachts common to-day there is less need than hitherto to split up the sail area; (ii) The efficiency of modern sail plans allows a hull to be driven by a small sail area, which may be disposed round a single mast in an easily handled rig without a long boom or bowsprit (we may recall that it was once considered faintly improper for a cutter's main boom to end short of the taffrail) and (iii) It is still as true to-day as it was when Dixon Kemp wrote it that " . . . of all the rigs which the ingenuity of man has devised, not one is equal to the cutter " (or, we might add to-day, the sloop) " for clawing to windward, reaching along the wind, or running down wind."

The single-masted rig, then, is the most probable choice to-day, and the variants of this will first be considered. They are: (i) Sloop; (ii) Masthead Sloop; (iii) Cutter; (iv) Masthead Cutter; (v) Masthead Sloop with lower forestay. An effective method of reviewing their qualities is to set them in turn above the same hull, using as the basis of comparison an equal rated sail area under the R.O.R.C. rule in each case. This has been done in *Fig. 2* (*a*), (*b*), (*c*), and (*d*). It should be remembered in what follows that

---

* *Excluding the now old fashioned jib topsail.*

equality of rating has been adopted to provide a logical comparison, not because rating is considered of primary importance; though obvious applications to ocean racing rigs will be apparent.

The sloop rig only became a seagoing proposition with the development of sail plans narrow enough to allow forestays to be set on or inside the stem. So long as the sloop had its forestay on a bowsprit, and hence had the whole rig depending on this spar and its bobstay, it could not be regarded as a good seagoing rig. Since the appearance of the inboard rig there has been, for small craft, a subdued rivalry between the sloop and the cutter, which like the ancient grudge ever threatens to break to new mutiny. And not surprisingly for the balance of advantages lies very evenly between the two rigs. Which to choose depends on a most careful analysis of the precise purpose of a boat, on the exact conditions under which she is to be sailed. Prejudice can blind; it never enlightens, and questions of rig are notoriously open to prejudiced answers.

The yacht shown in *Fig. 2 (a)* to *(d)* is 25 ft. on the waterline, has a displacement of 6½ tons, and carries 3 tons in the lead keel on a draft of 5 ft 6 in.—a very normal yacht of popular size. The sloop rig (*Fig. 2 (a)*), like the hull, is unexceptional. The mainsail is of moderate aspect ratio, the fore-triangle of reasonable size, and the staying plan is in accordance with good, modern practice. Details of the sails are thus:

Sail	Area	Outfit 1	Outfit 2	Outfit 3
Mainsail	320 sq. ft.	*	*	*
No. 1 Genoa	280 sq. ft.	*	*	*
No. 2 Genoa	230 sq. ft.	*	*	None
No. 1 Jib	175 sq. ft.	*	*	*
No. 2 Jib	130 sq. ft.	*	None	None
No. 3 Jib	90 sq. ft.	*	*	*

The wardrobe of headsails shown in Outfit 1 is a very full one, having sails carefully graduated in area from the biggest R.O.R.C. Genoa to a small jib having reef points. It would suit the intent racing owner with a long purse, and would give him the highest dividend on his rating investment. A reasonable economy would be to omit the No. 2 jib (Outfit 2). But Outfit 3, in spite of having only three headsails, would not only be adequate for cruising, but would not be a grave handicap when racing. Sloops have been successfully raced offshore with a wardrobe of three headsails—more are a luxury, not a necessity.

How does the cutter (*Fig. 2 (b)*) compare? It will be seen that it has a masthead rig, for surely this is the only sort of cutter that is sensible in small craft? Two sets of runners are an inconvenience in large cutters and absurd in small ones; yet a single set of runners with spans aloft is not sufficient to hold the luffs of two headsails taut. The cutter has a shorter mast than the sloop, which is an advantage; it is also more securely stayed than the sloop's, and with greater simplicity. There is no safer mast than the modern masthead cutter's with standing backstay, inner and outer forestays, two sets of spreaders, and all standing rigging adjustable from the deck.

The cutter, having a larger fore-triangle than the sloop, has a smaller mainsail. It is of slightly greater aspect ratio and hence higher efficiency area for area, and it has a shorter boom. Another feature making for easy handling is the more comfortable position of the runners, farther forward than in the sloop, easier to set up, and needing less slack when the boom is squared off.

The cutter needs more headsails. The sails in the drawing are those in Outfit 1 below, and Outfit 2 shows a more economical wardrobe:

Sail	Area	Outfit 1	Outfit 2
Mainsail	279 sq. ft.	*	*
No. 1 Staysail	125 sq. ft.	*	*
No. 2 Staysail	78 sq. ft.	*	None
No. 1 Yankee Jib	218 sq. ft.	*	*
No. 2 Yankee Jib	145 sq. ft.	*	None
No. 3 Yankee Jib	80 sq. ft.	*	*
Masthead Genoa	350 sq. ft.	*	None

There are thus six headsails, compared with the sloop's maximum of five, and two of these would be the very large masthead Genoa and the No. 1 Yankee jib. With the former set the cutter would spread a total area of 629 sq. ft.; with the latter and No. 1 staysail, 622 sq. ft. She therefore has an advantage in the area of canvas which she can set over the sloop, whose maximum is 600 sq. ft.

In theory the advantage in offshore racing lies with the cutter with its smaller mainsail, requiring less frequent reefing, its more flexible fore-triangle, and greater total sail area. But it is perhaps true to say that it is harder to sail a cutter at her best than a sloop. She needs more careful tuning, more refined sail trimming, and she demands more work from the crew when racing. The theoretical advantages of the cutter may be outweighed by the greater ease with which a sloop may be handled efficiently.

For cruising we would accept the second outfit of sails. Instead of the No. 3 Yankee shown we might preferably have one of 100–110 sq. ft., and the foot of the staysail might be shortened, allowing it to be set on a boom. The rig would then be exceptionally easy to handle with small sails abaft and ahead of the mast (the cutter's biggest headsail is

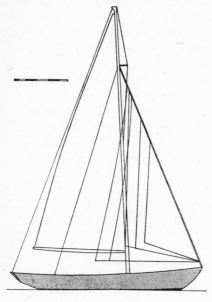

Figure 2 (a).—Sloop.

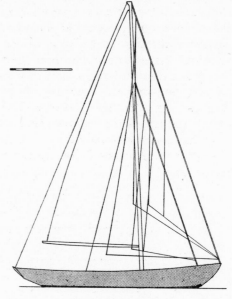

Figure 2 (b).—Cutter.

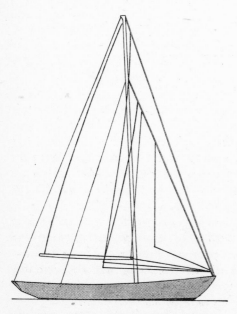

Figure 2 (c).—Masthead Sloop with inner forestay or " Slutter."

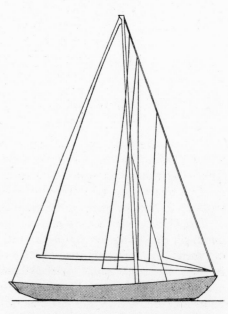

Figure 2 (d).—Masthead Sloop without inner forestay.

All the above rigs have the same rated (R.O.R.C.) sail area.

218 sq. ft. compared with the sloop's 280 sq. ft.) yet with a bigger total area than the sloop. And the cutter's advantages, of course, would become more pronounced in larger craft with bigger individual sails. The masthead cutter is, indeed, a simple, strong, and efficient cruising rig.

Between pure cruising and offshore racing, however, lies the evergreen sport of in-shore handicap racing—round the buoys. And here the sloop is at its best. The bigger mainsail is then an advantage, the headsails may be more quickly set and trimmed, and the spinnaker is easier to handle. The superiority of this rig for inshore racing was proved when for decades in the 8-Metre and 12-Metre classes, which reached such a high state of development, the boats remained obstinately sloop rigged; whilst even the J-boats, with their enormous fore-triangles, approached nearer and nearer to the sloop, and latterly sailed as sloops carrying double-clewed jibs.

We may now perhaps summarise the advantages of the sloop and cutter:

Cutter.   (i)   A better stayed mast and more easily tended rigging.
        (ii) A better cruiser as a result of (i) above, and of smaller and more easily handled headsails.
        (iii) Probably better for offshore racing if well-equipped with headsails and expertly handled.
Sloop.   (i)   Cheaper to equip and has fewer sails to occupy stowage space.
        (ii) Superior for round-the-buoy racing, and probably closer winded.
        (iii) Perhaps an easier rig to handle efficiently offshore.

The rig which has been christened slutter* (Fig. 2 (c)) is, we have seen, a masthead sloop with two forestays on which working sails may be set, one stay coming from the masthead and the other from a point lower on the mast, as in a normal sloop, and both leading to points on deck in the proximity of the stem head. For rating purposes a slutter therefore has a masthead fore-triangle.

The rig has the advantages of the cutter's small mainsail and large fore-triangle, whilst in harder weather it becomes a modest sloop with a headsail on the lower forestay. A disadvantage of the rig is the large outfit of sails needed. Those shown on the drawing are:

Sail	Area
Mainsail	279 sq. ft.
Masthead Genoa	350 sq. ft.
No. 2 Genoa	240 sq. ft.
No. 1 Jib	150 sq. ft.
No. 2 Jib	80 sq. ft.

* *Henceforward known in this book as a masthead sloop.*

The adjustments of areas in the fore-triangle, however, are very coarse as shown, and in a full racing outfit of headsails at least a second masthead Genoa is needed, and ideally a finer graduation of areas between the No. 2 Genoa and No. 2 jib. We thus need at least five headsails and perhaps six. The rig also presents serious problems in staying, for the mast must be strong enough to stand with the lower forestay let-go. Otherwise tacking with masthead Genoas is an impossibility; though the rig may be modified to the extent of having the lower forestay attached at the deck a few feet abaft the masthead one, when the big headsails may be passed with difficulty between the stays. But anyone who has done this a number of times in quick succession whilst short tacking will find himself favouring a different rig.

Designed as a purely cruising rig the masthead sloop has clear advantages. It is a sound practice for ocean-going to eliminate jumper stays and have instead a masthead forestay, adjustable from the deck, and providing a second line of defence to the lower stay in the forward support of the mast.* Working headsails will be set on the lower stay, which may be carried higher up the mast than in a sloop designed primarily for racing, and the topmast forestay will be used for light and reaching canvas. Boats of the Giles-designed Vertue class may be rigged either as conventional or masthead sloops, and *Vertue XXXV* did her extensive cruising under the latter rig. Eric Hiscock's *Wanderer III* also carries this rig, a further advantage of which for serious ocean work is the additional sheave and halyard at the masthead which it provides.

The masthead sloop with a single headstay (Fig. 2 (*d*)) offers the ultimate simplicity in rigging.† For certain types of yacht it is a tempting rig, but experience has proved that it is less efficient to windward than the normal sloop with its forestay at about 75 to 80 per cent of the mast height. This is due to the high jib altering the air flow on to the mainsail at the top, where the sail, due to its twist, is already at a very small angle to the wind, and producing a condition of no lift, or fluttering, at the head of the sail. There may be other contributory causes of the masthead sloop's relative inefficiency to windward, such as the greater length of forestay, and the longer unsupported length of mast below it, both of which encourage a less taut forestay. But if the necessary allowances are made for this in the design of the mast, the masthead sloop has advantages which the rarity of the type would suggest as not being recognised.

The Yawl.—By traditional definition the yawl has her mizzen mast stepped abaft the rudder post. This definition is unsatisfactory in its dependence upon the position of the rudder post, which is not a characteristic of the rig, and is directly misleading in this age of short-keeled yachts. The R.O.R.C. for the purpose of its rig allowances defines yawl and ketch thus: " If the afterside of the mizzen mast is forward of the after end of the waterline the yacht will be classed as a ketch; if on or abaft the after end of the water-line she will be classed as a yawl." This is altogether more satisfactory.

The primary object of two-masted rigs is to split up the sail area into individually smaller sails. The yawl is the first step in this direction and many cutters, especially in the past, became yawls simply by having their main boom cut down and a mizzen mast (often called a jigger) stepped in the counter. For many years the reputation of the yawl as a cruising rig was marred by bad design, the mainmast being stepped too far

See page 123.   † See page 121.

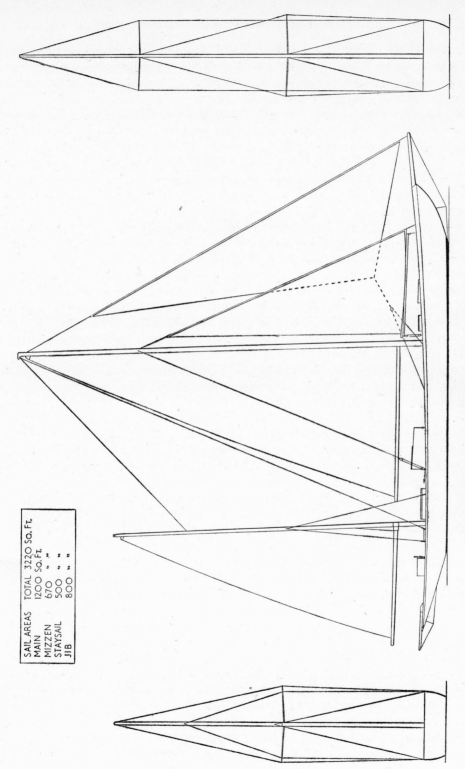

SAIL AREAS TOTAL 3220 SQ. FT.
MAIN   1200 SQ. FT.
MIZZEN   670   „   „
STAYSAIL   500   „   „
JIB   800   „   „

Figure 3.—Sail plan of *Erna*, Bermudian Ketch, formerly *Sumurun*.

forward, with a long, main boom which resulted in the mizzen being insecurely stepped too far aft in the counter. But there were in the past lovely examples of big cruising yawls; the Fife-designed *Sumurun* of 92 tons was one, which many years later, when her name was *Erna*, was re-rigged as a Bermudian ketch (*Fig. 3*).

The rig has been encouraged at different periods of yachting history by the advantages of rating which it has received under various handicapping systems. Thus alterations in the Y.R.A. time allowance scale produced a rash of yawls in 1899, and such great racing cutters as *Meteor*, *Satanita*, and *Ailsa* appeared under new yawl rigs. The success of the rig, even to windward, and especially that of the Kaiser's *Meteor*, which had had her 76-ft. mainboom shortened by 26 ft. in the process of the conversion, resulted in a sudden popularity of yawls for racing.

In our own day the R.O.R.C. rule has given a slight encouragement to yawls as a racing rig. To qualify as a yawl the mizzen must represent at least 9 per cent of the total sail area; then the rig allowance is 98 per cent. Compared with a sloop or cutter having a rated sail area of 900 sq. ft., a yawl with an equal rated area will have 936 sq. ft. of which at least 85 sq. ft. must be in the mizzen. The extra 36 sq. ft. of area would not alone justify the yawl for racing, though if a mizzen staysail is not carried a further 1 per cent reduction in measured rating is allowed. But the addition of a mizzen staysail, the area of which is entirely free of tax, makes the yawl a tempting proposition from the rating point of view.

To windward the mizzen of the yawl will be of little value. She is therefore left with 851 sq. ft. of rated area, excluding her mizzen, to pit against the sloop's or cutter's 900 sq. ft., for we are probably nearly right to say that such good as the mizzen does on the wind will only offset the windage of the mizzen mast and rigging. But her inferiority to windward will receive its compensation when the wind frees and the mizzen staysail adds 15–20 per cent to her rated area at no cost in rating. The choice between the single-masted rig or the yawl for racing is thus a matter of balancing the loss in ability to windward against the gain in reaching winds.

Mr. Adlard Coles' experiment in adopting the most modern form of yawl rig (*Fig. 4*) in so small a boat as *Cohoe II* (a fairly narrow craft of moderate displacement and a waterline length of 26 ft.) is of particular interest, and the careful analysis which he has made of his experience provides the most recent evidence we have on the characteristics of the modern small yawl. The design for *Cohoe II* started life as a sloop. A slight shortening of the boom allowed a mizzen mast to be stepped in the counter. In the balance Mr. Adlard Coles' opinion after the first season was against the rig for ocean racing and in favour of it for cruising. He has said, regarding the former:

" When close hauled the rig has little merit, for then the mizzen is not merely almost useless, but may be a positive hindrance by reason of the windage aloft. This is particularly marked in strong to gale winds over a long windward leg . . .

" Another point of sailing on which the yawl shows little advantage is when running before the wind . . . except perhaps in very light airs when any rag of canvas seems to help, or alternatively when one can effectively tack down wind.

" . . . there is little in favour of the rig (even when reaching) if the wind is strong enough to give all competing yachts their maximum speed . . .

" . . . It is reaching, of course, that the yawl shows so well. The mizzen staysail

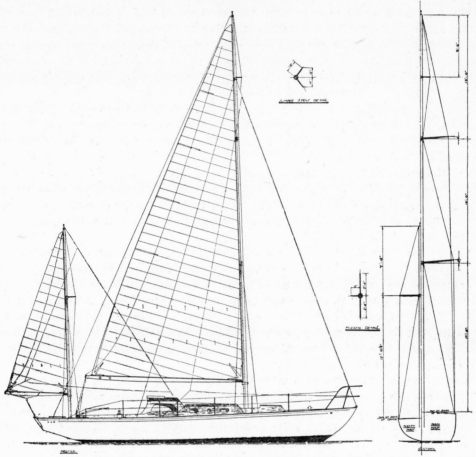

Figure 4.—Sail Plan of *Cohoe* II. The yawl rig applied to a Class III ocean racer.

makes an enormous difference . . . under the right conditions. But one does not always get the right conditions. The value of the rig accordingly depends simply upon the proportions which light to moderate free winds bear to the total wind conditions over the particular race or throughout the racing season."

The above would seem to be a most careful examination of the yawl as a racing rig to-day, but the following year a further experiment was made with *Cohoe II*. The mast was cut down to the jumper stays, the mainsail being reduced in proportion so that she became a masthead yawl. The reduction in mainsail area made the yacht sluggish in light airs, but strangely it had the effect of making her closer winded in a strong breeze, a quality not apparent in the first year. This was particularly marked in the Bay of Biscay Race of 1953, in which her owner states she proved to be the closest winded of the many yachts he has owned or sailed. This may be due to two reasons: the low mast making the yacht stiffer in a blow, and secondly the increase in the gap between the leech of the mainsail and the mizzen, so that the mizzen would be more effective. It was also said to have cured the rhythmic rolling to which this yacht was subject under her original rig.

What of the yawl for cruising? Its historic virtue remains; it is, of all two-masted rigs, the closest in performance to the cutter, whilst offering the advantage of smaller individual sails. But usually the sails of modern small sloops and cutters do not need to be further reduced in size, while the space occupied by the mizzen in craft below about 8-tons T.M., the weight of the mast, and the very considerable expense of its gear and rigging, are serious arguments against the rig.

Yet other advantages still remain. The yawl, correctly designed, is wonderfully easy to handle. She will sail and manoeuvre under mizzen and headsail only, or with the mizzen stowed; and under all plain sail is easily made self-steering by trimming the mizzen. The mainsail is small and will rarely need reefing. These are qualities of high value in the short, or single, handed cruiser. The larger yawl, with two headsails, becomes a snug sloop when the jib and mizzen are stowed. The small yawl with a masthead fore-triangle and twin standing backstays to the mainmast (the latter eliminating runners) has a combination of simplicity in rigging and easily handled sails which can hardly be bettered.

Yet the fact remains that modern small sloops and cutters do not usually need to have the size of their individual sails even further reduced; and as the price paid is less weatherliness and increased cost it will be clear why small yawls are not now common. Also, though most yawls will sail, as suggested, with mizzen stowed, or under mizzen and headsail alone—even such long-keeled, very heavy displacement types as the Falmouth Quay Punt will do so—there are yawls which lack this ability. There are those which sail badly, and cannot be persuaded to stay in even smooth water without a mainsail. But their number is becoming smaller.

It is the mizzen staysail which gives the keen edge to the virtue of the yawl, and to the ketch also. It is a sail for reaching or running with a quartering wind, a wonderfully effective one under these conditions, having great lift and power; and many yawls handle particularly easily and steadily under the combination of Genoa jib and mizzen staysail. The sail as a rule is set to the truck of the mizzen, and the tack is usually, though not invariably, secured off the centreline and on the weather side, this allowing the sail to be trimmed to a more effective angle.

The Ketch.—The ketch is the traditional English rig, but it is rarely seen in yachts which make ocean racing their first object, or in cruisers which wish to feel fast. Here sloops and cutters predominate, and it is on these rigs rather than on the ketch that the ingenuity of modern design has been expended.

The ketch carries a certain stigma of slowness; yet making all allowances for the rig's nature it would seem that this is due more to the fact that it is usually set above full-bodied cruising hulls of limited sailing ability, than to inherent lack of power in the rig itself.

The gaff ketch is undeniably slow and inefficient, for the sails are often of a poor shape and the gaffs sag badly, being too long as a result of the designer's efforts to secure the maximum sail area on short masts. In such boats the mizzen may be almost useless except with the wind free. The gaff ketch, furthermore, usually has an insecurely stayed mizzen, it being impossible to rig spring stays between the masts owing to the main gaff. But the Bermudian is free of these disadvantages and has many virtues. These include

the smallness of individual sails, the accessibility of the main boom, and a beautiful flexibility in the sail plan, which allows numerous, easily-handed combinations of sail to be
set ranging from a light weather spread of greater area than in any reasonable sloop or
cutter, to a small staysail and mizzen alone, under which the rightly designed ketch
handles and manoeuvres willingly. Ease of handling is accepted as one of the highest virtues
in a cruiser; but it may also be so in a racer. The easily handled ship is often the best-
handled ship.

   The rig is treated kindly by the R.O.R.C. rule; perhaps even with unmerited lenience
if a really efficient example of it is set above a hull of genuine sailing ability. Should
this be done the ketch seems to offer some surprising advantages for racing combined with
its numerous and well-tested abilities when cruising. In *Fig 5 (a)* and *(b)* we may compare
the ketch with a sloop rig, each set above a fast, modern hull of 27 ft. on the waterline
and fairly light displacement. The two rigs are designed to have the same rated area
under the R.O.R.C. rule—that is, the sloop's main and fore-triangle measurement of
510 sq. ft. is equally rated with the ketch's main, mizzen and fore-triangle of 577 sq. ft.
the value of $\sqrt{S}$ in the formula being 0.94 per cent of the square root of the rated sail
area for the ketch. To obtain this rig allowance the mizzen of the ketch must account
for at least 18 per cent of the total rated area, and in this example it is 23 per cent. The
basic design argument is set out in the drawing.

   Certain features of significance will be apparent. In area of canvas set, including the
150 per cent R.O.R.C. Genoa, the ketch carries 626 sq. ft. compared with 544 sq. ft.
in the sloop. Under mainsail and Genoa alone the ketch is able to set 491 sq. ft. Her

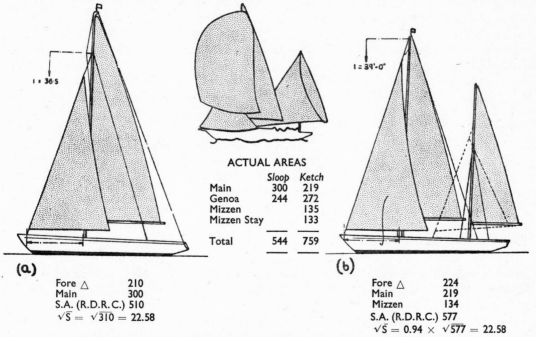

ACTUAL AREAS

	Sloop	Ketch
Main	300	219
Genoa	244	272
Mizzen		135
Mizzen Stay		133
Total	544	759

(a)

Fore △	210
Main	300
S.A. (R.D.R.C.)	510

$\sqrt{S} = \sqrt{310} = 22.58$

(b)

Fore △	224
Main	219
Mizzen	134
S.A. (R.D.R.C.)	577

$\sqrt{S} = 0.94 \times \sqrt{577} = 22.58$

Figure 5.—Comparative racing sail areas for a sloop and a modern ketch
of equal rated (R.O.R.C.) area.

fore-triangle is actually slightly larger than the sloop's, so she loses nothing in the size of her spinnaker. With the wind free, setting her mizzen staysail, she carries 759 sq. ft. compared with the sloop's 510 sq. ft.; and this additional 40 per cent of canvas costs nothing in rating.

With these advantages in sail area the ketch has a mainsail of only 70 per cent of the sloop's area, a Genoa bigger by about 15 per cent, and a fore-triangle supported by twin standing backstays which provide better support than the sloop's runners, and allow easier, more efficient handling of the ship.

To windward under full sail the ketch will be inferior to the sloop. But she has more sail in the fore-triangle, which on this point of sailing is the most effective place for it; her mainsail, per sq. ft., is more efficient owing to its greater aspect ratio; and to offset the greater windage of the rig she carries 82 sq. ft. or 15 per cent more sail area. The inferiority may not be serious.

It is in light winds, and particularly free, light winds, when the modern sloop can be such a heartbreaking creature to drive, that the virtues of the ketch are going to shine. And such winds are, after all, very common. Under these difficult conditions, when a light wind is playing over an old sea, the smaller, lighter main and mizzen of the ketch may be persuaded to remain asleep when the mainsail of the sloop is uncontrollably restless; while under all conditions of moderate, free winds the ketch, with its 40 per cent more sail area, will be formidably powered. If we take into account all the varied conditions met when racing off-shore it does seem that the flexibility of the well-designed ketch rig will allow it to face as many of them as effectively as the sloop of equal rated area.

The wishbone ketch is a variation on the basic ketch rig and appeared in *Vamarie*, built in Germany to designs by Cox and Stevens in 1933. *Jeanne d'Arc*, of 14-ton T.M., designed by Mr. Maurice Griffiths and built in 1951 for General Sir Frederick Browning, is a more recent example of the rig (Plate 13 and *Fig. 6*).

The wishbone ketch is the result of combining an unusual form of staysail ketch rig devised by Mr. F. Fenger (who was responsible for many other novelties in yacht rigs including a type of double spinnaker) with the wishbone spar invented by Nathaniel Herreshoff, and originally used by him for the booms of both mainsails and jibs. This type of boom was used as a gaff in *Vamarie*, and thus made the wishbone ketch rig possible.

The spar itself consists of two curved members each pivoted on a separate gooseneck on the mast about six to ten inches apart. The outer ends are connected by a metal cross bar of a length equal to the distance apart of the goosenecks, and hinged on the spars to allow movement as the wishbone swings. The vertical control of the wishbone consists of a standing topping lift from its outer end to the masthead, and a standing kicking strap from this same end to the mainmast at the tack of the wishbone sail. The angle of the wishbone is thus fixed. The sheet (or vang) is also led from the outer end of the spar, over a sheave on the mizzen mast, and down to the deck. The outhaul of the wishbone sail leads from a flat swivelling block at the outer end of the spar and thence along the gaff to its inboard end and down the mainmast.

Three main advantages are offered by the rig, though they are unfortunately married to severe disadvantages. The space between the masts is completely filled by canvas, this allowing the maximum sail area to be set on the masts. In no rig is the sail area so

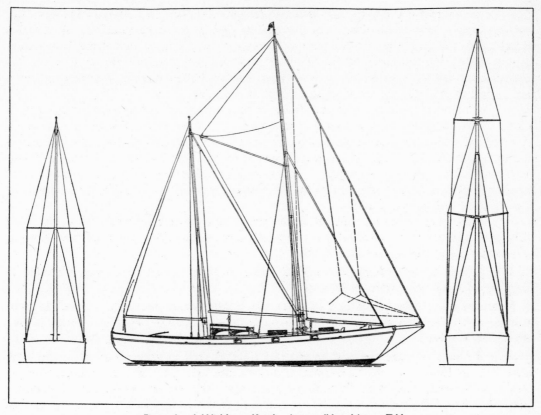

Figure 6.—A Wishbone Ketch. *Jeanne d'Arc*, 14 tons T.M.

completely divided and the individual sails so small for a given total area, with a result that above a certain size it is in theory the most easily handled rig. And this quality is emphasised by the fact that runners are not required in the staying of the masts.

The weaknesses of the rig lie at the heart of it, in the wishbone spar and its sail. The vang or sheet led down the mizzen mast does not alone give sure control of the heavy wishbone spar, permanently aloft, and additional vangs to the ship's side are needed. Thus simplicity is destroyed, but complete security is still not attained. Experiments have been made with wishbone gaffs in tracks, which may be lowered with the sail, but this arrangement has not been satisfactorily developed. The wishbone sail itself has been described by Mr. Sherman Hoyt, who knew *Vamarie*, as " . . . the most contrary contraption to handle, with the exception of a real parachute spinnaker on a ' J ' class yacht, that it has ever been my misfortune to be shipmate with." The sail becomes so difficult to handle, flogging violently when the outhaul is eased preparatory to lowering, and putting such a big strain in the gear and particularly the mizzen masthead, that the temptation is to hand it early; yet it represents a very big part of the sail plan's total driving power, and the yacht may then be undercanvassed.

The following notes have been prepared by Mr. Maurice Griffiths on the wishbone rig of *Jeanne d'Arc*:

E

" The wishbone ketch rig for *Jeanne d'Arc* was designed in collaboration with her owner, Lieut.-General Sir Frederick Browning, chiefly for easy handling by a light-weight crew. It was previously used on *Restless of Plyn*, a 32-ft. converted Mevagissey lugger, a heavy displacement boat of some 40 tons. Although the rig came up to expectations in having sails which were all very easy to set and handle, married to such a heavy hull the rig did not show off to its best advantage.

" With an easily-driven hull like *Jeanne d'Arc*'s the rig proved more practical and its closewinded qualities could be used to full advantage. The wishbone sail sets very much like a jib inverted and because of its height it is, like the Thames barge's topsail, the principal driving sail in the ship. When it is stowed it tends to reduce the sail area too drastically and it has been suggested that a second smaller sail should be set on the same track to give the equivalent of one reef. This, however, merely adds a complication which the rig has been designed to avoid.

" Apart from its undoubted efficiency when close-hauled and the relatively small area of all sails involved, so that each can be set and managed by one man, the following disadvantages of the rig are inescapable:

1. It is a poor rig for running downwind and a good spinnaker or Genoa is needed to keep up with normal cutters or sloops.

2. When running before anything of a sea the rolling causes the wishbone sail to gybe continually. The mizzen staysail is also unhappy and unless guyed out tends to flap from side to side.

3. It is difficult to make the wishbone spars light as well as strong enough. Although alloy fittings have replaced the original ironwork one light pair of spars collapsed under strain. The spars, therefore, have to be stout and their weight so far aloft becomes a problem when gybing continually. The snapping of the vang which leads to the mizzen masthead could be very serious and some form of snubber or shock cord at the foot of the mizzen mast had to be introduced.

4. Whether the wishbone spars are made in spruce or light alloy, together with their knuckle joint fittings they are a considerable expense, and they are liable to breakages through gybing.

5. In heavy weather with the wishbone stowed the divided spar is still aloft and presents considerable windage in addition to its weight and tendency to shake badly.

6. Perhaps the greatest disadvantage of the rig is its staying. The main masthead backstay, the wishbone vang, and the mizzen staysail halyard all lead to the mizzen masthead. To hold this the mizzen masthead stay, which leads to the sternpost, is responsible for all this varying strain. The whole stability of the rig, therefore, depends on this mizzen masthead stay. If it parts there is every chance of the mizzen mast being whipped out of the ship and the main mast following if prompt action is not taken. This mizzen stay is especially stout with robust iron fittings and it is carried down to the sternpost instead of to a bumpkin or outrigger for the sake of strength. I should, however, be very unhappy to have to trust to it in offshore cruising or racing.

" I believe the American wishbone ketch *Vamarie* had trouble with these stays, while the parting of the vang controlling the wishbone was the cause of the complete collapse of the masts in the similarly rigged 83-ft. *Wishbone*.

" For sailing in sheltered waters, therefore, this rig can be described as very good fun and exceptionally easy to control; but its inherent weakness with the wind aft seems to me to make it unsuitable for serious offshore sailing. I have no doubt that *Jeanne d'Arc* would sail very well indeed as a normal Bermudian ketch, for with this rig she could set slightly more canvas. As a Bermudian stemhead cutter she would, I think, be better still."*

The Schooner.—The schooner, of all rigs, trails its clouds of glory. Perhaps the majority of the greatest and loveliest yachts have been schooners, whose like will never be seen again. For a large yacht it is probably the most seaworthy rig in the world, offering a well-split sail plan and one which allows progressive balanced reductions in canvas, eventually enabling her to be hove-to under foresail alone.

This rig is better liked in America than in Britain, though we have noted that even there the ketch is now the more popular. However, Mr. John Alden wrote in a latter a few years ago: " After having two ketches I have rather gone back to liking a schooner, though it is a hard rig to race . . . " Nobody has a greater experience of the schooner both from the drawing table and the cockpit than this designer. But for yachts of the sizes popular to-day the rig does not have much to offer, whilst it does have ineradicable disadvantages. The small schooner has never been favoured on this side of the Atlantic as it has been in the U.S.A.

The chief faults of the rig may be summarised thus:

(i) Compared with a sloop, cutter, or yawl it is slow to windward. Though the rig allowances of the R.O.R.C. and C.C.A. suggest that it is superior to the ketch, it is likely that the modern well-designed ketch is at least the equal of the well-designed schooner.

(ii) It is slow running before the wind owing to the blanketing effect of the mainsail. As a result it is more profitable in the schooner than with any other rig to tack down wind, and except when it is blowing hard these tactics are necessary if a reasonable speed is to be maintained.

(iii) A schooner is difficult to handle when running before the wind, the effective sail area under these conditions being too far aft.

(iv) An extensive sail outfit is needed, which is expensive in any yacht and occupies precious space below deck in small yachts.

(v) The two masts, stepped in the middle part of the ship, make difficulties when planning the accommodation, particularly in small schooners.

A big part of the schooner's weakness lies in the sails between the masts. Originally this was a gaff foresail, which of necessity was a narrow sail, with a result that its gaff sagged many degrees farther to leeward than that of the mainsail. It was a poor sail on the wind and partly accounted for the schooner's inefficiency. When Bermudian mainsails

* *Whilst this book was in the press Mr. Frederic A. Fenger mentioned in the course of a letter some recent points about his type of ketch rig, which he has described as " The most criticised rig." He wrote:*
" *I have developed this rig to what I believe is as high a state as one will find in any of the present-day rigs. It has been quite simple: (i) The split-sprit or ' wishbone' in my sail goes up and down with it, as in any gaff sail; (ii) As a result of proper proportioning of the various sail units—using a largish mizzen with its mast stepped well into the vessel—and not exaggerating the area of the main trysail, the rig stresses have been reduced to a minimum, so that a permanent backstay is no longer needed.*"

were introduced gaff foresails tended to remain, and many schooners are rigged thus to-day; for a Bermudian foresail, whilst obviating the problem of the sagging gaff, does not allow enough area of canvas to be set between the masts.

Vangs may be used to reduce the sagging of the fore gaff, but in 1924 a more radical solution to the problem was offered, by the American designer Starling Burgess, in the schooner *Advance*. Instead of the normal foresail a small, triangular boomless one, like a jib, was set on the foremast, and—also like a jib—this sail was trimmed with double sheets. A main staysail was set on a main forestay, and above these two sails a topsail was set between the masts a little below the trucks. Subsequently Herreshoff devised a rig in which there were four separate triangular sails between the masts which completely filled the space.

From such rigs the staysail schooner developed, having a main staysail and above it a large Fisherman staysail. When set flying the latter sail is difficult to handle, but in many schooners it is set in a track on the foremast. The staysail schooner is more close winded than the earlier type, and it is a convenient combination of cruising and racing rig for large craft. A variety of sails may be set between the masts, and even light weather kites from the mainmast head to the stem or bowsprit; whilst the rig is made easily worked for cruising by handing the Fisherman staysail.

*   *   *   *   *

The varieties of the fore and aft rig under which yachts sail are still, even to-day if we extend our survey beyond the yachting centres, almost infinite; but when the power of tradition and the natural pressure of conservatism have spent themselves it will perhaps become clear that, for small craft, the fore and aft rig has reached its highest state of development in speed and safety in the modern sloop, cutter, yawl, and ketch.

3

RIGS AND RATING RULES

IT is possible to believe to-day that some of the rating rules in force tend, in their methods of measuring sail area, towards complicated nonsense. One designer, who has devoted much time to studying the rating rules which have appeared since the war and in analysing their effect on design, has been ready to call them " a jumble of prejudices."

This matter is not only of interest to racing men. Forty years ago yachts were poisoned by bad rigs, with masts far forward and enormous mainsails and mainbooms; and this at a time when the Brixham trawlers—many of them cutter rigged—had no such defects and offered an example to follow. The modern, beautifully easily handled sloop and cutter are in part the product of good rating rules and of the beneficial influence of methods of measuring sail area upon the design of rigs. For the rules governing the sail area measurement of racing yachts strongly influence the character of the rigs which racing yachtsmen have to handle; and this influence spreads to all types of yachts. Evidence of it is to be found in the sail lockers of the purest cruisers.

The apparently simple operation of measuring sail area is attended by many pitfalls. As in hull design, methods of measurement, or restrictions placed on features which are thought to be undesirable, may produce unexpected results. Limitations have a habit of creating rather more problems than they solve.

The rating rule which for many years influenced the design of sail plans, and did much to produce our modern rigs, was that of the International Yacht Racing Union governing the inshore 6, 8, and 12-Metre classes. It was in operation for the major racing classes during the 1920-39 period, when rigs, guided by the new aerodynamic theories, underwent such drastic changes. Important features of the rule were embodied in that of the R.O.R.C., where its influence was even more far-reaching.

Under the I.Y.R.U. rule the total height of the rig was limited in each class. That of the fore-triangle might not exceed 75 per cent of this height. Here we may see immediately an important influence of rule upon the development of rig. During the years when the inshore classes were racing with relatively low fore-triangles, the lack of any such limit upon height in the R.O.R.C. rule was allowing the seagoing virtues of the masthead rig to be learned. Had the I.Y.R.U. rule's limit on fore-triangle height been in force for offshore craft the lesson might have been missed; for it is well known that most innovations develop under the stress of racing.

The most controversial point in sail area measurement concerns the fore-triangle. The difficulty of measuring exactly an area of canvas led to the 85 per cent fore-triangle rule—a rig rather than a sail measurement in fact—by which the area of the headsails was assessed as 85 per cent of the area of the triangle formed by the fore side of the mast at the deck, the point where the line of the luff of the foremost headsail cuts the decks, and the top of the highest sheave in the mast used for headsails. As headsails which do not overlap the mast—and they did not do so to any extent when the rule was formulated —have an area of about 85 per cent of this triangle, the rule gave a fair approximation to the actual area of canvas; but without the inconvenience and incidental inaccuracies of measuring the sails themselves.

Inevitably the system of measurement influenced designers, who will always put sail area where it is cheap in terms of rating. With overlapping headsails this place became the fore-triangle. The effect of the 85 per cent rule was gradually to force the mast back in the boat. This gave two advantages in terms of rating: with headsails having a greater actual area than 85 per cent of the fore-triangle the bigger fore-triangle allowed more free area to be obtained. It also enabled bigger spinnakers to be carried, for their size was limited by the fore-triangle measurements. One 6-Metre, the *Atrocia*, appeared in 1927 with an enormous fore-triangle, her mast abaft amidships, and a tiny mainsail; but she was an aberration from the main line of development, and the rules were modified to preclude such extremes—probably unnecessarily as the rig was not successful.

Whilst racing his 6-Metre off Genoa in the same year the Swedish helmsman Suen Salen broke out an overlapping jib, and to everyone's surprise carried this large headsail round the whole course. This was not the first appearance of such a sail. Balloon jibs were known in the earliest days of yachting, and were presumably copied from the reaching jibs and staysails sometimes carried in fishing craft—the Brixham trawler's Mumblebee for example. Yachts of the 1880s sometimes carried outfits of impressively overlapping headsails.

Yet Salen's Genoa jib was new in principle. The Mediterranean has borne sails of many surprising shapes on its waters since Ulysses deserted the lovely Calypso and sailed away leaving the Great Bear on his port hand. But none of them was the Genoa jib as set in Salen's 6-Metre, which was sheeted in hard when the boat came on the wind and proved itself to be a sail which revolutionised the technique of working a boat to windward. For the old overlapping jibs and ballooners were of light canvas and cut with a very full belly for sailing off the wind. The Genoa developed into a sail made of heavy canvas, cut flat, and designed primarily for sheeting in hard for windward work. The new Genoa proved its fitness so strikingly that it not only revolutionised the sails carried ahead of the masts of racing yachts, but became too an essential part of the outfit in cruising yachts.

The reason for the Genoa's remarkable efficiency was already, in 1927, explicable scientifically. Two years earlier the results of experiments by Warner and Ober in the U.S.A. had revealed the now so well-known fact that, area for area, a headsail is much more efficient than a sail set abaft the mast. The conclusions were obvious. By extending the jib abaft the mast extra area was obtained, and the most efficient sail in the ship was made larger without any price in the rating being paid for the gain. Cruisers, even those uninterested in their rating, found in the Genoa a sail which allowed them to increase their sail area on masts no longer than they needed for their working sail. The Genoa, in fact, is a convenient sail, though it may sometimes be a difficult one to handle, giving greater elasticity to the sail plan and a more seamanlike rig.

The result of Genoas and the 85 per cent fore-triangle measurement was that the masts of yachts were gradually, by a process of evolution over the years, moved back. The valuable lesson was learned that yachts became more easily handled, more docile, and more efficient with the mast well away from the bows. But no extremes developed under the rule. Masts remained comfortably ahead of amidships without being uncomfortably far forward.

The R.O.R.C. adopted the 85 per cent fore-triangle measurement, but with no limitation on the height of the fore-triangle. The overlap of headsails was limited to 50 per cent of the base of the fore-triangle,* and thus large Genoas and headsails were encouraged. Yachts became better balanced, and the advantages of a small mainsail and a large fore-triangle, in which carefully graduated sail adjustments could be made, were appreciated.

At the same time, it became necessary to carry a great number of headsails finely graduated in area. This was an expense. The actual area of the largest Genoa might be twice its rated area under R.O.R.C. measurement. In the I.Y.R.U. Metre classes it was about 70 per cent greater than its fore-triangle measurement. The total area of canvas carried by yachts was from a third to a fifth more than the area for which they were rated. And apart from their expense these great headsails were hard to handle, making it necessary to carry more and better crew.

The R.O.R.C. rule remains unaltered to-day. The 85 per cent fore-triangle measurement still holds, and the expense of large and numerous headsails is accepted. But designers have great freedom in drawing their sail plans, and the rule has produced some of the most seaworthy rigs that have ever been devised.

After the war there was a revulsion in inshore racing against the expense of big headsails and the crew needed to handle them. The great influence of the late Mr. Charles Nicholson was brought to bear strongly against the 85 per cent fore-triangle measurement, which was considered to be guilty beyond redemption, and in the new rating rules then introduced—that of the Cruiser-Racer classes, and of the 5.5-Metre class—different principles were adopted in the measurement of sail area. Their object was the elimination of big headsails. The rules have not yet been tested for long enough to be sure whether they will produce this economically desirable end, without destroying the good balance of modern rigs. But certainly freedom in design has been singularly restricted by a number of complicated new measurements.

In the I.Y.R.U. Cruiser-Racer rule the total height of the rig, as in the old I.Y.R.U. rule, is limited. There is a bonus for heights below the maximum and a penalty for those above, but the first is not tempting enough and the second is too stringent to encourage any wide departures from the stipulated figure. The height of the fore-triangle is limited, which precludes the masthead rig, but in this rule the height has been raised to 80 per cent of that of the rig. This is a reasonable acknowledgement of modern trends. Unlike the old I.Y.R.U. rule this one sets a limit on the base of the fore-triangle of $\sqrt{\text{Sail Area}}$ —an obscure and fussy complication. The actual area of the fore-triangle is used for rating purposes; that is it is assessed at 100 per cent of its area. As under the R.O.R.C. rule, the overlap of the sail on the mast may not exceed 50 per cent of the fore-triangle's base. It will be seen that the fore-triangles and headsails of the Cruiser-Racers are rigidly controlled.

In the 5.5-Metre rule the maximum height of the rig is limited; likewise that of the fore-triangle, and again to 80 per cent of the rig's height. The base of the fore-triangle is controlled, and may not exceed 0.5 $\sqrt{\text{Sail Area}}$, so that, as in the Cruiser-Racer rule, with an increase in sail area the base may be increased. But in this rule the area of the fore-triangle does not enter directly into the rating, and the actual area of the headsail

* Known as the " 150 per cent " fore-triangle.

is measured: " . . . half the length of the luff multiplied by a perpendicular from the luff rope to the clew when hauled hand tight and when folded double on the luff." Not surprisingly, the rule specifies that the luff rope must be of wire. The fore-triangle area affects the rated sail area simply through the stipulation that no headsail may be of *less* than 80 per cent of this area.

What will be the effect on design of these new rules, whose innovatory clauses on sail measurement are specifically aimed at killing large fore-triangles and headsails? In the earlier I.Y.R.U. rule, and in that of the R.O.R.C. under which such sails developed, sail area in the fore-triangle was cheap. Comparisons between the rules are approximately as follows:—

(i) Under the old I.Y.R.U. rule, and the R.O.R.C. rule, it is possible to set approximately $1\frac{1}{4}$–2 sq. ft. of headsail per sq. ft. of rated area.

(ii) Under the Cruiser-Racer rule it is not practicable to set more than about $1\frac{1}{8}$ sq. ft. of headsail per sq. ft. of rating.

(iii) Under the 5.5-Metre rule 1 sq. ft. of sail area costs 1 sq. ft. of rated area.

It will be seen that the rules become, in the order given, progressively harder on headsail area. Under the old 85 per cent rule the incentive to gain cheap sail area forward was strong enough to produce rigs with a good balance between their fore and after canvas, and with the mast stepped comfortably but not excessively far back in the ship. The 5.5-Metres are small craft, and perhaps we need not worry if their sail plans develop undesirable tendencies towards large mainsails and small headsails, and the rule has the 80 per cent fore-triangle safeguard against tiny jibs. But it is questionable whether this crop of new restrictions does anything but hamper design. In the cause of economy it may be desirable to eliminate large, overlapping headsails, and the need to carry a big range of such sails to suit various wind strengths. It is not easy to see why the obvious method of doing this—a simple reduction in the maximum amount of overlap permitted—was not adopted, instead of the radical departure from existing methods of sail measurement which had served well.

The R.O.R.C. rule states: " If the horizontal distance between the tack of any headsail, when new, and a perpendicular dropped from the clew of the sail exceeds one and a half times the base J, two-thirds of the excess shall be added to J." The Cruiser-Racer rule contains the same stipulation: " The distance between the foremost point of the base of the fore-triangle and a perpendicular dropped from the clew of any headsail (except spinnakers) is not to exceed 150 per cent of the length of the base of the fore-triangle." The Cruiser-Racer rule, by its new, complicated fore-triangle measurements may encourage undesirably small fore-triangles, but the root of the trouble—the amount of overlap of the headsails—remains as before. The obvious legislative course would surely have been to retain the older, more simple fore-triangle measurement, and to limit the overlap to 120 per cent of the base of the fore-triangle, or less if desired.

Under the C.C.A. rule headsails are measured in two ways: for cruising canvas the fore-triangle is assessed at its actual area and " no headsail can be of a size that, considering 'made' dimensions, would extend aft of the forward side of the mast to which they are set." This means that the actual area of canvas is paid for pretty dearly.

Under the regulations for racing canvas the fore-triangle is more costly, for it is rated in excess of its actual area as a triangle, the measurement, simply expressed, being 0.6 (Base × Height). But there is a penalty for height of fore-triangle which comes into operation when the height exceeds twice the base, and this will produce an addition to the area given by the basic formula of perhaps 10 per cent.

If we consider a fore-triangle in which, under R.O.R.C. notation, I=40 ft., J = 16 ft., the rated area is 272 sq. ft. Under the C.C.A. rule for racing canvas the area would be 416 sq. ft. But with this rating the C.C.A. rule sets no limit to the Genoa overlap— " Under Racing Canvas Rating there is no limit to headsail width dimensions."

The C.C.A. rule in all its aspects is an imposing document, and nowhere more so than in its stipulations regarding sail measurements; though whether, in the end, they lead anywhere profitable seems at least questionable. As in the fore-triangle there is an aspect-ratio penalty in the mainsail, which comes into force at ratios above two. The rule leads a designer into a mass of calculations, encourages him to try a very low aspect ratio mainsail and a bowsprit (which are the implications of the rule) and in the end probably returns him to a normal and efficient sail plan regardless of the penalties attached to it—which is perhaps to the credit of the rule. But it is a weakness that the rule piles up calculation, the import of which is a fore and aft distribution of the sail area entailing a return of bowsprits and the elimination of standing backstays.

In the International 5.5-Metre class the rash of restrictions has also spread to the mainsail, but without the C.C.A. rule's excuse of having to assess handicaps. It is stated: " The breadth of mainsail at half of lengths of luff and leach may never exceed 60 per cent of length of boom, and three-quarters of those lengths is not to exceed 35 per cent." Since the rule contains the normal batten restrictions, which for many decades have effectively controlled the roach in the mainsail, the object of this added provision is obscure. An eminent authority, himself partly responsible for this rule, has confessed that *he* cannot understand the reason for it.

Apart from its treatment of the fore-triangle, there is another feature of the I.Y.R.U. Cruiser-Racer rule, which is questionable. This is the virtual prohibition of two-masted rigs. The prohibition is not explicit; but it does seem surprising that a gathering of experts should have failed to see that their treatment of yawls and ketches is tantamount to their banishment from the class. The reason lies in the method which they have adopted for measuring a mizzen staysail. It is measured by the same formula as the fore-triangle:

$$\frac{I_2 \times J_2}{2} = \text{Area}$$

" Where," to quote the rule, " I_2 is the distance from the top of the deck at covering board level to the point where the luff of the staysail cuts the mast, and where J_2 is the distance from the foreside of the mast to where the line of the luff of the sail cuts the deck at covering board level."

The area of the mizzen staysail is thus included in the rated sail area. It is true that the part of the sail lying abaft the fore side of the mizzen mast escapes measurement. The part lying forward of the mast, however, appears to be grossly over-assessed; for the foot of the sail will probably have to be cut high enough to clear a doghouse, and the tack will be secured not at covering board level but on the top of the coach-roof. It seems not impossible that the absurdity will arise of a mizzen staysail being rated at *more* than its canvas area. This, however, is a small point compared with its being rated at all.

Clearly, no yacht can afford to include in her rated sail area a sail which is of use only in free winds, and which has to be lowered and re-hoisted on every tack or gybe. It would mean that whilst beating to windward a yawl or ketch, already suffering from inherent disadvantages on this point of sailing, would be further handicapped by setting about 20 per cent less sail area.

If we treat the Cruiser-Racers primarily as inshore classes intended to sail together without handicap, there may be arguments for prohibiting two masted rigs altogether—though not, one feels, very strong ones. But the existing conditions under which yawls and ketches are to be forced to sail suggests that a situation has been produced which the rule makers did not intend.

It is understood that abroad there are yawls which have been built to the International rule, and which now find themselves virtually useless as class boats; and apart from the expense of scrapping the rig, conversion to a cutter is sometimes an impracticable operation without rebuilding the ship inside. How difficult is the work of International rule makers; and how chancy the occupation of designing and building boats to the rules!

4

THREE RIGS

ERNA first appeared as *Sumurun*, a 90-tonner of 79-ft. L.O.A. and 63.5 ft. L.W.L., designed by Fife and built at Farlie for Lord Sackville in 1914. She had a yawl rig typical of the period with a total sail area of 5,580 sq. ft., a tall mainmast with fidded topmast carrying a very large gaff mainsail and jackyard topsail, and a relatively small mizzen mast stepped well aft in the counter. Her hull was vintage Fife, with his incomparably graceful sheerline, unexaggerated, beautifully formed ends, and hull lines capable of calling up admiration forty years later. She was converted to a modern, more snug Bermudian ketch rig of 3,220 sq. ft.—a reduction in area of 42 per cent—to designs by the author when the yacht was in the Mediterranean in 1951 (*Fig. 3*).

In yachts of every size one of the hardest problems when converting the rig may arise from a necessity to alter the position of the mast. Apart from the structural problems involved, this may lead to difficulties in the accommodation, and in small craft to the disorganisation of the whole internal layout. In *Erna* these complications fortunately did not arise. Her mainmast, at one-third of the waterline length from forward, was suitably placed for her new ketch rig. The re-stepping of the mizzen mast might not have been so easily arranged. The engine prevented it being stepped any farther forward than is shown, and skylights on deck and a bulkhead below presented further obstacles; but allowing the necessary clearances it was possible to step the mast in a position which enabled a satisfactory balance between the fore and after canvas to be achieved.

The object of the conversion, as it so often is to-day in large craft, was to provide a simpler, more easily handled rig, compensating to some extent for its loss in area by a greater efficiency, whilst giving to the ship, in alliance with the powerful auxiliary, some of the characteristics of a Fifty-fifty. The bowsprit was shortened by about 7 ft., the mainmast with fidded topmast replaced by a shorter, hollow stick of Oregon pine, on which was set a mainsail of 1,200 sq. ft.—the maximum that was considered desirable—and instead of the original yawl's mizzen with its boom extending far beyond the counter, the yacht was given a mizzen of high aspect ratio with its boom end reasonably accessible.

The two-headsail rig with the jib set on the topmast forestay was a compromise. The admirable masthead rig is more satisfactory in a stem-head cutter of 20 tons than in a 90-tonner with a bowsprit. An alternative to the arrangement shown would have been a three-headsail rig with a jib topsail set flying above the staysail and jib. This would have necessitated either two sets of runners, which were not wanted, or the older-fashion layout of headsails with fore and jibstays coming to points close together on the mast, and hence capable of being supported, though not very efficiently, by one set of runners. The latter rig was seriously considered before the existing one was chosen, and though less efficient it might have had advantages in a large yacht used purely for cruising. There would, however, always have been the temptation to save the trouble of handling an extra set of headsail sheets by keeping the jib topsail in its locker, and *Erna*'s total area is not big enough to allow such sacrifices.

The mainmast is securely stayed with twin standing backstays led to each quarter abreast of the mizzen mast, and the scantlings of the mainmast, which has only a moderate amount of taper to the masthead, were designed to carry the loads of the rig without anxiety. Both the main and the mizzen were new hollow spars of Oregon pine.

*   *   *   *   *

Verona (*Fig.* 7) was a more difficult problem. She was built as the *Xarifa*, a 276-ton gaff ketch with a sail area of 8,362 sq. ft. designed by Soper and built by Camper and Nicholsons in 1912. In 1925 this firm prepared drawings of a gaff schooner rig for the yacht, these showing the conventional rig of the period with fidded topmasts, gaff main, narrow gaff foresail, and jackyard topsails. This rig was never adopted, but subsequently the yacht was converted into a Bermudian ketch. She was later bought by Mr. E. Powys-Cobb, whose brother, Mr. Wheatley Cobb, had saved from the shipbreakers the 38-gun frigate *Trincomalee*, renamed *Foudroyant*, the preservation of which was later undertaken by the National Maritime Museum.

The new rig of *Verona* was to drawings prepared by the author, the work being done when the yacht was lying in Cape Town. Before work was started on the drawings the owner wrote: " I am undertaking *Verona*'s restoration largely for the pleasure of preserving a fine specimen of a fine period in yacht architecture, much as my Father saved churches and castles and my brother the ships *Foudroyant* and *Implacable*." *Verona*'s three-masted rig was the result of close collaboration between Mr. Powys-Cobb and the author, and to the owner and the devoted study which he gave to the problem are due many of its original features.

A comfortable, economical cruising rig was wanted capable of being handled on ocean passages with a small crew. Reasonable windward efficiency was required, but more important was the ability to handle well in fair ocean winds. The three-masted staysail schooner rig suggested itself for so large a ship, though alternatives were tried, including one with a square rigged foremast. The three-masted staysail schooner had already become well known in *Cetonia*, originally a two-masted gaff schooner, which had been converted to the former more easily handled rig by Lord Stalbridge. In 1927 the same rig had appeared in the 700-ton *Creole* by Charles Nicholson.

The weakness of the *Cetonia–Creole* rig lay in the triangular mainsail and foresail— the heart of the whole conception. Though efficient when sailing on the wind these sails, with their sheets led down the mast astern, became progressively less effective as the wind drew aft, the lead to the centreline preventing the sheets exercising any proper control of the flow in the sails in free winds. The sails became bags, and as a result were of little use when most needed. They were also difficult sails to hand in any weight of wind; yet they represented a big proportion of the total area, and a yacht was undercanvassed without them. It was wished to avoid these faults in *Verona*.

Various methods of solving the problem were studied, including an arrangement of sheet horses on the gaffs to improve the leads of the main and fore sheets. The incidental problems raised did not seem amenable to a seamanlike solution. The use of wishbone gaffs on the two sails were considered, but experience with these pieces of gear, and in much smaller yachts, did not encourage their use. Finally, the unusual sail plan shown was chosen. The mainsail and foresail were divided into two by gaffs hinged on goosenecks

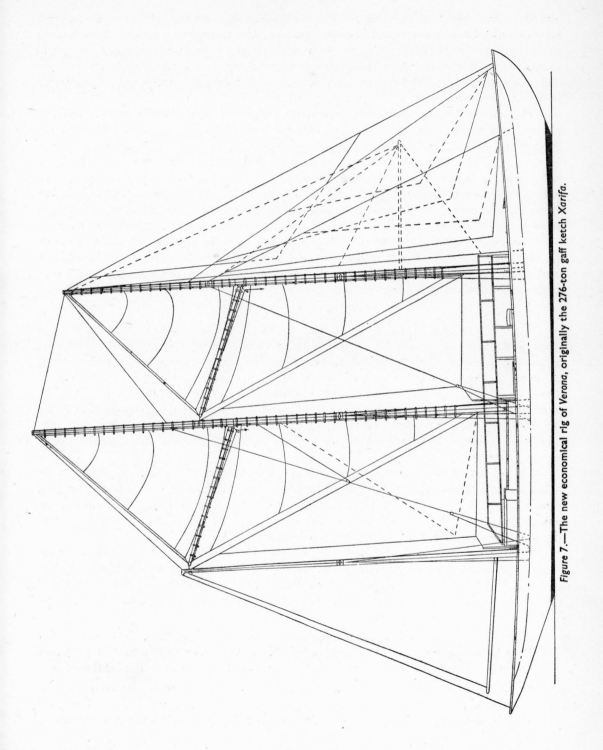

Figure 7.—The new economical rig of *Verona*, originally the 276-ton gaff ketch *Xarifa*.

and kept permanently aloft. This allowed each of the sails to be of smaller area, enabling sail to be shortened in better graduated stages, and also solved the problem of controlling the sails when off the wind. The problem remained, though in a less aggravated form than it would if the heavier wishbone gaffs were fitted, of ensuring control of the gaffs aloft under the worst conditions. The solution entails the use of vangs on the gaffs, and sheets of great strength.

Though set on mast hoops the mainsail, foresail and their topsails are not handed but are brailed into the mast. The normal method of brailing a boomless sail, in which the head of the sail remains extended along the gaff, the upper part of the sail being drawn up to the gaff and in to the mast by brails, at the middle of the gaff and at the throat, is not applicable to triangular sails of *Verona*'s shape. Here the outhauls of the lower sails and topsails are let go, and the sails brailed into the masts. The heads of the mainsail and foresail are controlled by their hoop attachment to the gaffs, but this arragement may not allow so tidy a stow of the sails to be made as with the orthodox brailing arrangement.

The owner was anxious to eliminate, so far as possible, booms in the rig, and the staysails were therefore cut to allow boomless sheeting to wide horses spanning the cat walk. This obviously entailed a loss of efficiency as well as area, but was a necessary part of the process of compromise.

*   *   *   *   *

Since the second World War, and at intervals before it also, efforts have been made to transform radically the orthodox methods of converting wind power into propulsion. It has been justly observed that in spite of all the study which has been devoted to yachts during half a century, particularly in the application (and mis-application) of aerodynamic data, speeds under sail have not materially altered during this period. The most significant advance has been the substitution of low, broad, gaff-headed sails for tall, narrow triangular ones. In terms of ease of handling the advance has been tremendous; in terms of speed, taking an average of all conditions, this hardly exists—except in the case of dinghies.

Yet no recent experimenter has produced and proved any radically new rig, or hull-rig combination, able to show both higher speed and greater ease of handling, and combining both of these with seaworthiness, than the modern Bermudian rig. This, however, is what the Vosper–Hasler Lapwing rig may offer. Unlike other experimental rigs it is not only radical in conception, but designed for the sea.

The origin of the rig lay in Colonel H. G. Hasler's conviction that the Bermudian rig was not the best method of converting wind power into boat propulsion; though he agreed that in the balance it was nearer to the ideal than any of its predecessors. He enumerated the objections to the Bermudian rig under nine headings, and these, it will be seen, go deeply to the roots of the matter:

(i) Shortening sail and making it again demands skilled work on deck, much of it forward of the mast where it is hazardous and uncomfortable and produces exhaustion in the crew. This tends to keep yachts in port in doubtful weather.

(ii) When shortening sail in a quick blow a yacht is often more or less out of control, and all hands have to fight flogging sails and wire at the price of some danger. At night gear readily becomes foul, adding to the confusion. If a halyard is accidentally let go it may be necessary to go aloft to recover it. In a seaway this is always dangerous, and physically impossible for the majority of yachtsmen.

(iii) With the Bermudian rig gybing is an essential evolution. In strong winds it needs a skilful crew and helmsman; whilst the threat of an unintentional gybe is a constant worry in boats of all sizes. In practice this results in helmsmen luffing up to get the wind on the quarter, which puts the boat off course and also at a less effective angle to the seas than when running dead before them.

(iv) With the wind abaft the beam neither the main nor headsails can be prevented from drawing, since it is impossible to spill the wind out of them; so there is no way of reducing speed quickly except by lowering sail. This causes many complications when manoeuvring in confined waters.

(v) The Bermudian yacht's necessary wardrobe of headsails is expensive, requires a great amount of stowage space, and is difficult to keep aired. The problem of dealing with wet sails is always present.

(vi) Efficient sailing with the wind aft demands a spinnaker, which is hard to set and hand, and prevents any sudden manoeuvre.

(vii) Parachute spinnakers which sheet round the forestay need constant tending and are uncontrollable in a steep, quartering sea, when they tend to chafe to pieces, and may get foul aloft.

(viii) To make a cruising boat steer herself downwind it is necessary to hand both the main and parachute spinnaker and to set twin, flat spinnakers or twin staysails. This involves yet more sails, gear, and deck work, and ends in even less ability to manoeuvre quickly.

(ix) The mainsail lies heavily against the lee rigging when the boom is squared off. This introduces chafe, which, if continued for any length of time at sea, results in a short life for the mainsail. In practice, the mainsheet is usually kept pinned in a little when running in a seaway, though this increases the probability of an unintentional gybe.

It will be seen that the above criticisms fall broadly under two headings: the complications in the gear, sails, and handling of an orthodox rig at sea on all points of sailing; the difficulty of making the fore and aft rig perform well when the wind is aft, and the further complications resulting from this. But there is another matter stressed by Hasler: " There seem to be strong reasons for suspecting that aerodynamically the Bermudian rig is not very efficient." This undoubted inefficiency has resulted in many experiments with rigs, and, since the war, in efforts to adapt the rigid aerofoil to the propulsion of boats. The Vosper–Hasler Lapwing rig is an attempt to combine good aerodynamics with the obvious seagoing requirements which are needed in any rig—the most important of which is the ability to make progressive reductions in sail area. None of the purely aerodynamic solutions of the rig problem has satisfied the requirements of a sailing craft at sea.

The Vosper–Hasler Lapwing rig was designed to satisfy the following requirements, and in the order of priority given:

(i) To be fully seaworthy for ocean passages.

(ii) To allow all sail handling, reefing, and furling to be carried out from the cockpit.

(iii) To give double the sail area for running down wind to that carried comfortably by the boat to windward in about Force 3.

(iv) To be not less efficient than a normal Bermudian sloop in all wind strengths and on all points of sailing.

A detailed analysis of the various experimental rigs which have appeared from time to time over a period of many decades revealed only one which seemed to offer a foundation for a new conception, and able to fulfil the above requirements. This was the Ljungstrom rig, which was experimented with elaborately during the Thirties, though not on the whole successfully. It was the invention of Dr. Frederick Ljungstrom, and consisted of an unstayed mast (except for a standing backstay) which was rotatable, and on which was set a boomless mainsail cut with heavy roach in the foot. This sail was double, and the two parts were separated and goosewinged when sailing off the wind. Furling and reefing the mainsail was achieved by rotating the mast and rolling the sail round it, and this solved some of the problems of handling which are inherent in the Bermudian rig. There was difficulty, however, in stretching out the clews of the boomless double mainsail when off the wind, and as with most loose-footed mainsails the sheeting problem was not easy to solve efficiently. The Vosper–Hasler Lapwing rig takes its departure from the point where Dr. Ljungstrom's rig was finalised. It emphatically is not the Ljungstrom rig, and the principles of its operation are widely different; but a debt is owed to the pioneer work on the earlier rig.

The important features of the rig are shown in *Fig. 8.* The circular mast is unstayed, and is supported by bearings at the step (A) and at the partners (B). Rotation is effected by a wheel on the mast (3) operated by a rope working in a V-groove. The mainsail is double, the two parts having a common luff which is secured to the mast.

The lower part of the mast is sheathed in a metal tube (4) coming well above the deck and thereby reducing the unsupported length of the mast, and carrying also the fittings of the twin cantilever booms. Each boom is supported by a bearing ring (C) near the top of the mast tube and another (D) round the housing of the upper mast bearing. The booms can therefore neither lift nor droop, but are capable of being opened, like the legs of a pair of dividers, at any required angle to one another; or alternatively they may be locked rigidly together.

Each boom carries a clew traveller (6) running in a track along the top of the boom, and hauled out by a traveller outhaul operated by a small drum winch (E). Also on each boom is a wire clew outhaul (7) leading from the clew of the sail through the clew traveller to a second small drum winch (F). When the booms are together the winches may be locked so as to turn as one.

The mainsheet consists of an endless, single-part rope leading from the starboard boom through a saddle hook (G) to a sheet winch (H) and then round forward of the mast and back to a second winch and saddle hook and so to the port boom. If the sheet is released from the winches and saddle hooks the booms are free to swing right round the mast.

The sails are made of stiffened fabric which is only just flexible enough to be rolled round the mast. The fabric is intended to be water- and mildew-proof, to have a polished surface on both sides, and to be airtight. The luffs of the sails are battened to the mast and no halyard is fitted.

The leeches of the two sails are cut straight in their lower parts, and run into a big roach at the head, this being for reasons connected with the geometry of reefing. To support the roach, if the sailcloth is not stiff enough in itself, vertical battens may be fitted as shown. At the truck is mounted a large hardwood bullseye, through which a burgee halyard is kept rove. This can be used to send a heavier rope aloft if one is required as an emergency halyard or gantline.

It will be evident that the handling of this rig follows a technique widely different from that practised with the normal Bermudian sloop. To windward the differences are less radical than when sailing off the wind. The twin mainsails and booms lie closed and together, the principal control of the sails being the mainsheet, but the rig allows a finer control of the set of the sails than is normally possible, and greater manoeuvrability.

Firstly, by slightly turning the mast, it may be arranged that the luff of the sail leads off the mast on the lee side (*Fig. 9*) which is in accordance with sound aerodynamic principles. The arching of the sail may be controlled precisely either by working the clew outhauls or by turning the mast slightly; and a further adjustment is provided by the alterations which may be made in the angle of the clew outhaul by altering the tautness in the outhaul and the position of the traveller. By using the twisting action of the mast the stiff sail can be made to hold a good firm arching, even in ghosting weather when a soft sail collapses, and the sail itself has very little twist as a result of its shape and the high-cut clew.

The boat may be sailed on any point of the wind with the sails closed (*Fig. 9*), the arching and exact trim of the sails being adjusted in the ways explained above. Also, on any point of sailing, the sheet may be let go, allowing the sail to weathercock (*Fig. 10*). When weathercocking the mast is given an extra twist to stretch the sail taut; and in this condition there is no drive from the sail and the boat may pick up a mooring down wind, or set sail before leaving the mooring though the boat may be tide rode and the wind fresh. The sail simply lies quietly and with hardly a flutter. Here we see an important element of the powers of manoeuvrability offered by the rig.

It is also possible with this rig to make a stern board whilst still under effective control of the boat. This may be done in one of two ways, as shown in *Fig. 11*.

To reef or furl, the traveller outhauls are released and the mast rotated. The travellers are then pulled in by the clews of the sails, and it is not usually necessary to touch the clew outhauls. To shake out a reef or set sail the mast is released and the travellers hauled out, the sail thus being unrolled from the mast.

When reefed the sail will not usually be re-rolled the opposite way round the mast each time on tacking; but if the aerodynamically ideal lead of the sail be desired—say for a long board in open water—this may be done by bearing away for a few moments, so that the sail will not flog, and re-rolling the sail.

The boat may be hove-to by bringing the boom amidships or slightly to windward, and by varying the exact trim it is possible to produce any desired amount of headway or drift.

F

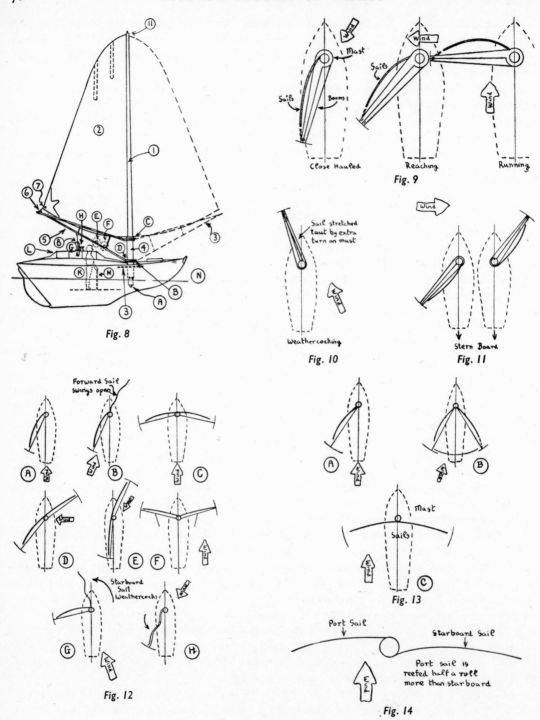

Fig. 8

Fig. 9

Fig. 10

Fig. 11

Fig. 12

Fig. 13

Fig. 14

Figures 8 to 14.—The Vosper–Hasler Lapwing Rig.

In all the above conditions the boat is sailing with only half her total area of canvas effectively exposed. When sailing with the wind anywhere from a close reach to dead astern the sails may be opened out, and the greater area of sail which a boat is capable of carrying in free winds becomes readily available without the setting of additional, complicated sails, and the reeving of their gear. To open the sails the boat's course is squared off to a run whilst the sails remain closed and the mainsheets are fairly hard (*Fig. 12 (a)*). The sheet of the lee boom is then released from its saddle hook and winch, and pulled taut round the fore side of the mast. The catch connecting the booms is released and the boat run momentarily by the lee, this resulting in the leeward sail being blown round the mast (*Fig.* 12 (*b*)), when it is hauled aft by its sheet.

The sheets are then trimmed as required for the point of sailing, whether running (*Fig.* 12 (*c*)), reaching (*Fig.* 12 (*d*)), or close reaching (*Fig.* 12 (*e*)). In light weather the two booms may be latched together at an angle (about 210°) which holds the two sails on a continuous fair curve. They may be swung as one, in the manner of trimming a squaresail; and in this condition it is impossible to gybe accidentally. The windward sail, even if it gets aback, will not swing across the ship.

To close the sails, one sheet is let go and its boom allowed to blow round the bow (*Fig.* 12 (*g*)). The boat is then luffed until the sails come within reach of the helmsman (*Fig.* 12 (*h*)) when the booms are latched together and the sheet of the forward boom picked up and brought back to its own winch again.

There is another method of opening the sails. The boat is run off the wind as before, and with the sheets fairly hard (*Fig. 13 (a)*). The catch connecting the booms is released and the weather sail gybed open, as the boat is run momentarily by the lee, by jerking on the sheet (*Fig. 13 (b)*). It will be seen that at the end of this evolution the mast lies to leeward of the sail, whereas previously it was to windward. As it is probable that aerodynamically the mast is more harmful in this position than to windward a point is scored against this method of opening the sails; but it is still possible to obtain a fair and continuous curve between the two sails (*Fig.* 13 (*c*)). To close the sails again it is simply necessary to gybe one on top of the other.

The sails may be reefed with the booms open, but this entails going forward to the mast to work the clew controls, and if single-handed it is easier to close the sails, reef them, and open them again, all of which may be done without leaving the helm. When the sails are reefed whilst open one side will always have half a roll more than the other, and the fact that the mast must cause a break in the fair curve of the two sails tends to discourage the use of reefed, open sails when the wind is on or forward of the beam. This is little handicap as the sails would not then normally be opened in strong winds on these points of sailing (*Fig. 14*).

· 5 ·

MASTS

A MAST, fresh in its new, Spring varnish, being dressed by a gang of riggers as it lies on the trestles in the yard, is surely one of the best of all the fitting out sights? Masts are attractive objects; but lying row on row in their winter racks, bare of rigging and covered in dust, they lose their innate romance (for consider how much of human history is associated with the mast) and become simply Brobdingnagian billiard cues. But move them into the sunshine and the life which is in them begins to revive. So do a number of troubles.

Masts are tricky things. It is not for nothing that Lloyd's, which is ready to specify the scantlings of nearly every other part of a yacht, washes its hands of them altogether and plants the responsibility for their size and shape squarely on the designer's shoulders; then, as a happy afterthought, advises him to fit lightning conductors. The advice is good; but it leaves the part between the lightning conductor and the step open to various interpretations. The fact that Lloyd's, with its vast collection of data on wooden yachts, feels like this about masts, suggests that masts are perhaps a little beyond rational analysis.

Variable Factors.—A variety of factors influence the stresses which a mast has to carry. The fundamental one is the displacement of the boat, this being the chief determinant of the stability, and hence of the load which the spars and rigging will have to bear. Other factors are those involved in the complete picture of the stability—the ballast ratio, draft, and stiffness of the hull form—and the rigging features, especially the spread of the shrouds, which determines the compression put in the mast when setting up the rigging, the arrangement of the forestays and the drift of the runners.

These various features will modify the preliminary choice of the mast scantlings based on the displacement of the boat. Thus spreaders which are wider than usual, a low fore-triangle, and runners carried far aft will allow a reduction in diameter for a given displacement. A masthead sloop of the same displacement, with standing backstay but no runners or inner forestay, must have the scantlings increased.

The exact distribution of pressure over a given sail plan cannot be certainly known, and hence the resultant forces acting at different points on the mast can only be judged. The complex relationships of the stresses in the shrouds and stays, additionally complicated by the sails set on many of the stays and the loads carried by the sheets, make a system of forces which is beyond exact mathematical treatment. Also, such calculations do not take into account the sudden stresses which occur in a seaway, the magnified forces which come into play when a yacht is heeled suddenly by a squall which lets up for an instant, and then renews itself and strikes again as she is swinging back to the upright.

Allowance has also to be made in seagoing yachts for failure of part of the rigging. J-class yachts lost their masts in a few moments whilst a runner jambed on its winch, or when a rigging screw failed aloft. Masts must be able to stand against minor rigging failures.

With wooden masts there is also the uncertainty to be faced of the exact strength of any given timber, which varies widely with the conditions of seasoning and growth. Probably the masting of the J-class *Enterprise* was studied as carefully as that of any boat. Prior to the fitting of the duraluminium mast with which she eventually raced, she had two wooden masts of identical external shape and scantlings but of different wall thicknesses. The thinner-walled mast should have been 8 per cent lighter than the heavier. In fact, owing to the different density of the woods, the thicker-walled one was lighter than calculated and the other heavier; but there was still an appreciable saving in weight. After sailing with the lighter mast, which noticeably improved *Enterprise*'s stability, Vanderbilt reported that it was as stiff, if not stiffer, than its predecessor.

Weight and Shape.—Except when masts are cut from the solid tree and dressed to size and taper—a process rarely adopted to-day—the round shape has been replaced by sections having a greater scantling fore and aft than athwartships. Owing to the relative sparcity of fore and aft staying compared with that of athwartships this gives the best disposition of material to resist the stresses to which it is subject. With the same object of disposing a given amount of material in the way which produces the greatest strength, the hollow mast is adopted in preference to the solid. To-day the hollow mast will probably be cheaper also.

A rather absurd situation arises in the International Dragon One Design class, in which solid masts are statutory. Builders in their efforts to produce the strongest, lightest solid mast are forced to adopt elaborate methods of construction, involving the scarphing and shaping of numerous separate pieces of timber, which in the end costs more than a hollow spar of less weight and greater strength. Where very large masts are concerned, the availability of suitable timber, or of the skilled labour, may raise problems in constructing a hollow mast which result in solid ones proving the more economical. The fore and mizzen masts of the three-masted schooner *Verona*, for example, are solid (*Fig. 7*). A quotation for three hollow masts, without fittings, was more than £2,500, excluding their transport to Durban where the yacht lay. In this case solid masts built on the spot proved the cheaper; though a hollow mainmast was adopted.

The hollowing of a mast produces a higher ratio of strength to weight than is possible in the solid. A round solid mast $3\frac{5}{8}$ in. in diameter has the same strength as a hollow one 4 in. in diameter and with walls 1 in. thick; but is almost double the weight. A solid mast of 4 in. diameter is 50 per cent stronger than the hollow one, but is more than double the weight. The reason for hollow masts and spars will be obvious.

The sectional shape of a mast has to be considered from an aerodynamical point of view as well as from that of strength. The direct wind resistance on a mast is unimportant compared with its effect on the airflow around it on the mainsail. Since the wind never comes from dead ahead when sailing, oval and pear-shaped masts have a greater wind resistance than round ones. Round masts also cause the least disturbance in the airflow on to the sails (if we exclude rotating masts) but the structural advantages of the other two shapes justify their adoption.

Between the oval and the pear-shaped mast there seems little to choose aerodynamically. The area presented to the wind, when close hauled, by a pear spar is less than that of an oval one. The pear allows a smoother flow of wind on to the windward side of the sail, but it causes more disturbance to leeward. Since the driving power of the leeward side is about twice that to windward, disturbance to this side is more harmful, and though it may be less in degree, it is probably more damaging. This is suggested by the fact that model tests on mast interference show that with a thin, round mast, its disturbing effect is least injurious when it lies to windward of the sail.

Mast Scantlings.—The principal factors governing mast sections are:

   (i) Displacement.
  (ii) Ballast ratio.
 (iii) Stiffness due to hull shape.
 (iv) Height of fore-triangle.
  (v) Angle of spread of shrouds.
 (vi) Fore and aft staying.
(vii) Unsupported length of mast panel.

Stability is a function of displacement, and it is the outstanding criterion of the stresses which a mast has to carry. *Fig. 15* shows curves, based on displacement, indicating suitable scantlings for hollow, spruce masts. Two curves are shown, and the point between them indicating the most suitable scantling for any displacement is fixed by reference to the other features of the hull and rig.

The chief effect of hull shape on mast loading lies in the initial resistance to heeling, and in the quick motion of a stiff yacht, which produces greater momentum in the mast during a roll, and the more sudden destruction of this momentum at the end of each roll. Yachts under tow or power have been dismasted from this cause.

The criterion of stiffness is the metacentric height, the metacentre being easily and quickly found by calculation. Below is given, for a range of yachts, the height of the metacentre above the waterline, expressed as a proportion of the waterline beam. It will be seen to vary between 0.54 in a scow of the Thames Rater type and 0.156 in the old *Genesta*, an extreme example of the plank-on-edge shape.

Yacht	Proportion of Beam at L.W.L.
Genesta (plank-on-edge)	0.156
Dorade (narrow ocean racer)	0.244
Conewago (8-metre)	0.246
Z 4-tonner (small cruiser)	0.281
Stormy Weather (ocean racer, moderate beam)	0.303
Mystery (Robert Clark 11-ton cruiser)	0.312
Fidelis (8-ton cruiser)	0.329
Satanita (162-rater)	0.347
Windermere 17-ft. class	0.408
Thames Rater	0.542

The above ratios are indications of initial stiffness and quickness of motion. Together with the ballast ratio, which will range between 0.2 in small, heavily built cruisers, and 0.6 in the 6-metres, and with the displacement, a complete picture of the mast stresses caused by the hull design may be obtained.

The height of the jib halyard sheave (the top of the fore-triangle) may be anywhere between the masthead and about 65 per cent of the mast length above the deck, depending on the rig. The higher the fore-triangle the greater must be the mast scantlings to carry the increased compressive loading of the forestay. This will be the result firstly of the steeper angle of the stay, and secondly of the greater tension needed in the stay to keep it straight, its length and the area of sail which it carries being greater.

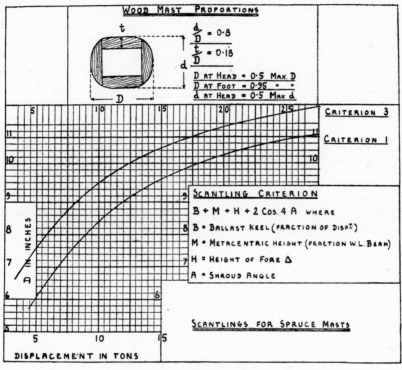

Figure 15.—Mast Scantling Curves.

Similarly a small angle of spread to the shrouds increases the compressive loading in the mast, and also the tension in the shrouds. The angle is measured between the centre-line of the mast and the shroud, and the object of spreaders is simply to produce as big an angle as possible. The rate at which the mast and shroud loading varies with the angle of spread is shown in *Fig. 16*. The common range of shroud angles is between 15° and 20°, and it may be seen that the larger angle reduces the loading by about 33 per cent.*

The width of the spreaders will be governed by the cut and trim of the headsails. Modern headsails need narrow spreaders for their correct sheeting, and this means dividing the mast into shorter panels if the stresses in mast and shrouds are not to be excessive. When a Genoa is not carried the most effective staying for a small mast, giving the least windage, lightest weight, and offering the greatest security and ease of handling, is a single, wide spreader.

* See page 110.

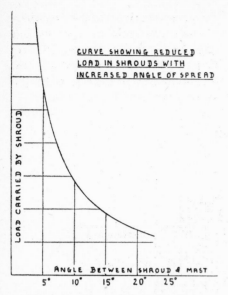

CURVE SHOWING REDUCED
LOAD IN SHROUDS WITH
INCREASED ANGLE OF SPREAD

LOAD CARRIED BY SHROUD

ANGLE BETWEEN SHROUD & MAST

5°   10°   15°   20°   25°

Figure 16.—Mast and Shroud Loading.

Another feature governing the mast scantlings is the drift of the runners. The farther forward they are, the easier it is to handle the ship, but the compressive loading in the mast is increased for a given forestay tension.

The complex relationships of these variables prohibit rigid rules being made for the determination of mast scantlings. The empirical formula $B+M+H+2Cos4A$ may be used when determining the point between the two curves which indicates the scantlings for a given displacement. In this formula, the four most important factors apart from displacement are combined to produce a scantling criterion, which will range between 1 and 3, the values respectively of the upper and lower curves. The formula and key to the symbols is also given in *Fig. 15*.

The difficulty in establishing a formula of this kind lies in the weighting of the various factors so that they bear the right relationship to one another. Twice the cosine or four times the shroud angle is used in the formula. It should be noted that when determining this factor the shroud angle must be multiplied by four *before* the cosine is looked up in a book of tables. The cosine found is then multiplied by two. Thus, if the shroud angle is 15°, four times the angle is 60°, and the cosine of this is 0.5. The value of the factor is twice this, i.e., one.

The fore-triangle height is measured as the proportion which this height, above the mast's mid-point, bears to half the mast's length. Thus, the value for a masthead rig becomes one, and for a rig with the forestay 80 per cent of the mast height above the deck, it is 0.6.

When the maximum fore and aft scantling of the mast has been determined, the other proportions may be fixed by reference to the data given above the curves in *Fig.* 15. The method of construction shown, in which the mast is built of four staves, from which the taper is taken before glueing up, is now very popular for all sizes of hollow masts. The scantlings will apply to other methods of construction.

It was once the usual practice, which is still often adopted, to taper Bermudian masts to a diameter at the head or truck of half the maximum diameter. This is sometimes excessive save in lightly stressed mizzen masts on which a mizzen staysail is not set. Then the stresses in the masthead are produced only by the small area of canvas near the peak of the mizzen, and these are slight. Yachts with fore-triangles to the masthead are heavily loaded at this point; and in boats with a lower fore-triangle, having jumper stays opposing the pull of a standing backstay, the stresses in the masthead may be even higher than in the masthead rig. This is due to the small angle of the jumper stays to the mast, and the consequently high compression load which they induce. As a result, masts excessively tapered in their upper length are hardly justified with modern rigs; their persistence would seem to be a matter of tradition. To-day values of D and d at the masthead of 0.65 of the maximum D and d are acceptable, D being the fore and aft dimension, d that athwartships.

Masts are usually slightly tapered from the point of maximum D to the heel, and the size at the heel may suitably be 0.95 D. But since the saving of weight in the lower part of the mast is comparatively unimportant, and anyhow is small in quantity owing to the slightness of the taper, it is preferable in craft of 20 tons and more to make the lower mast parallel. This allows the heel to have the maximum bearing surface, and hence reduces the compressive load per square inch on the step.

As in so much concerning masts, the necessary wall thickness is best judged empirically. We may derive a general rule based on the best examples of masting, and this is as serviceable as any other guide. One rule, based on an analysis of many successful masts, gives the maximum wall thickness as 18 per cent of the maximum fore and aft axis. Sometimes the aft stave of the mast is made thicker than the other three, this compensating for the weakening caused by the numerous track screws, and also giving them a stronger grip. The ratio of wall thickness to maximum D should be about 0.18, but may drop a little below this value for the forward and side staves of the mast if the after one is increased. An average value of 0.18 should be maintained.

Another rule, originating I believe in the Olin Stephens office, allows the thicknesses of the end and side walls to be 20 per cent of the fore and aft and athwartship axes respectively. If we take a mast of average proportions this rule produces similar results to the former. Wall thickness may be varied along the length, tapering like the mast itself towards the head. But in most masts the internal tapering is not worth the effort and the walls are of equal thickness everywhere.

The oval spruce mast designed by Laurent Giles for *Cohoe* is shown in *Fig. 17*, and will serve as a further guide in designing the masts of cruisers and offshore racers of the popular, small size. The scantlings are the same as those for the wooden masts of the R.N.S.A. 24-ft. class, and though *Cohoe* does not carry her fore-triangle to the masthead, the scantlings are sufficient for this. *Cohoe*'s displacement in racing trim is about 4 tons.

Fig. 18 shows a large hollow spruce mast—that designed for *Verona**—and the method of construction is revealed in some detail. Here the

*See Fig. 7.

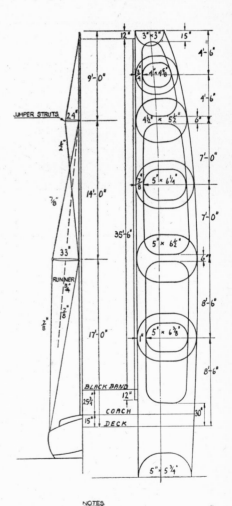

NOTES
TRACK BUTTS PLACED AT PANEL POINTS
MAIN HALYARD SHEAVE 3½ . ⅜

Figure 17.—Mast Plan, Cohoe I.

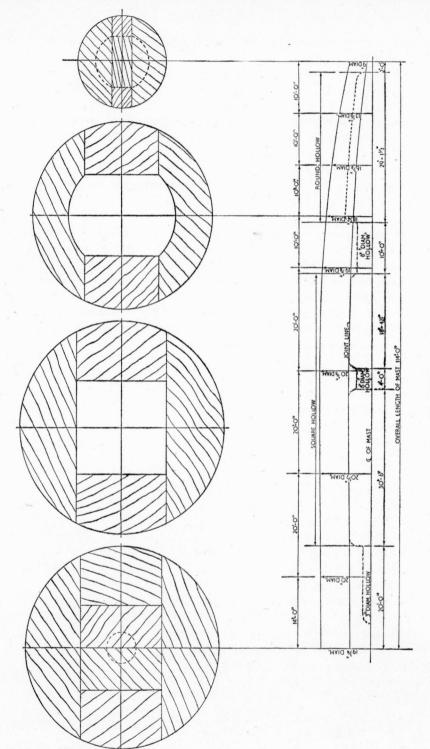

Figure 18.—Verona's mainmast.

wall thickness is, in general, slightly in excess of that specified above, except at the corners of the square internal hollow of the mast. The saving of weight was unimportant in this case, and it was considered preferable to allow for any abrasion resulting from the working of the mast hoops on the soft spruce.

Masts Stepped on Deck.—For some years the stepping of masts on deck has been becoming more common, and this system received its benediction for ocean-going work when *Vertue XXXV* crossed the Atlantic with hers mounted in a socket on top of the coach-roof. The one advantage of stepping it on deck is the inches saved in the cabin by substituting a slender metal pillar for the bulky heel of the mast; and these inches may make the difference between an awkward squeeze and a comfortable passage through to the forward accommodation.

The chief disadvantage of a mast stepped on deck is that for an equal breaking load it must be of appreciably heavier scantlings than one stepped into the hull. The application of ordinary mechanical theory, such as the engineer uses when calculating strengths, to the masts and rigging of yachts is fraught with difficulties, and no sensible figures relating to mast strengths have been published. One method of comparing mast strengths—and it is better regarded as a comparison than a sum to obtain numerical values—is Euler's formula, used in general and shipbuilding engineering for calculating the strength of pillars and long columns.

A mast stepped in the hull gains strength from the rigid fixing of the lower part of the mast between the partners and the step. The effect of it being held firmly at these points reduces the freedom of the upper part of the mast to bend. A simple experiment with a couple of garden canes will reveal this fact more readily than mathematics. If a pressure is applied directly downwards on to a stick 2 ft. in length having its lower end resting on a hard path it will be found to bend more readily than one 2 ft. 6 in. long with the lower 6 in. stuck into the lawn.

The same applies to masts, and using Euler's formula it may be shown that for equal strength a mast stepped on deck has to be about 25 per cent heavier than one stepped into the hull, the extra weight being due to the larger diameter needed. Owing to the complex influence of the staying this figure cannot be relied on fully; but the general truth remains. To obtain the same degree of stiffness and security a mast stepped on deck must be heavier than one buried in the hull, and the staying must be more complete. In seagoing craft, for example, twin standing backstays may be considered essential.*

The Construction of Masts.—In the construction of hollow masts we seem to have moved with the years from complication and elegance to such complete simplicity that many of the best masts to-day are long tapered boxes with the corners rounded. Records indicate that the first hollow mast was one 92 ft. long belonging to the American sloop

*Mr. W. E. W. Crealock, M.I.C.E., disagrees with the above, but his third paragraph suggests that he does not do so completely. He writes: " An essential assumption for all fixed ended column formulae is that the end should be rigidly fixed, but that is certainly not the case for a boat's mast, especially in the case of yachts with the modern extended cabin-top with no through beams for the greater part of their length.

" In some designs I have known, the cabin-top is strengthened by two bent angles in way of the mast; but bent angles do not even approximate to a rigid frame unless stiffened by plate gussets or similar devices, for which there is seldom space.

" It should perhaps be added that in good, modern construction the rigidity of the hull in the vicinity of the mast partners may be ensured by structural bulkheads and plate knees rather than wrought steel angles."

Maria in 1845, and this was built with staves and bound with iron hoops like a barrel. Nathaniel Herreshoff developed a similar method of construction, though without the hoops, and it proved, not surprisingly, to be very expensive, great skill being needed to taper and fit the staves.

Nearly a century later the simple box form of mast was arrived at. With normal wall thicknesses a perfect oval is not obtained by this method, but in terms of weight for strength there is a gain owing to the greater section modulus obtained with the flatter sides and blunter ends. In larger masts the end staves may be rebated to take the sides and a hardwood spline may sometimes be fitted along each glued joint, though the value of this seems rather doubtful. Again, in some larger masts corner posts may be fitted. These allow the wall thickness to be maintained whilst rounding the ends of the mast more easily; the radii of the ends may then be equal to half the mast's width.

A great advantage of the box construction is that the wall thicknesses may be varied independently of one another. Thus the strength may be arranged where it is most wanted, which means in the end staves, the mast being less well supported fore and aft than athwartships, and the after wall being weakened by the screws fastening the track.

Hollow masts may also be made from two planks whose combined thickness is equal to the mast's diameter (*Fig. 17*). The two parts are tapered and hollowed, then glued together, after which the spar is rounded. This is one of the earlier methods of making hollow masts, and is still much used.

The quality of such masts depends on the accuracy of the hollowing, which has to be done with gouges and small planes. Francis Herreshoff in his *Common Sense of Yacht Design* gives a rather alarming photograph of a section through one mast made in this way, showing a considerable variation in the wall thickness due to careless hollowing. In one part of the section the wall thickness is twice that at another and it is varying round the whole circumference. One feels that this mast must have been made at the same time as the Liberty Ships and even more quickly. Usually a shipwright will make templates on the inside of the mast, spaced at intervals along its length, and carve the inside accurately to them. But there remains the shaping of the outside, and with this method there is certainly the possibility of slight variations in wall thickness.

Some masts are hollow from a few inches above the gooseneck to a few feet below the truck. Others have solid webs, or at least a slight thickening of the walls, in way of the major fittings, such as spreader sockets, shroud tangs and the like. There are two schools of thought on whether or not to have such webs.

At one time they were commoner than they are now. When shrouds are spliced round the mast they are essential to prevent crushing of the mast walls; but with mast bands or the strap type of tang, having one or more through bolts and the stresses spread over a big area of the walls by the straps and wood screws, shrouds may be securely anchored without solid webs. It is argued that the solids introduce sudden interruptions in the strength of a mast, hard spots as it were, which weaken rather than strengthen it; whilst the shrinking and swelling of the wood in way of the solids encourage failure at the glued joints. The latter argument has strength when glues which are not fully waterproof are used.

But the advantage of webs, apart from their compensating for the strength lost as a result of through bolts and wood screws, is to add stiffness to the mast at a small cost in weight. With standing rigging set up as hard as it is to-day, it is difficult to make light masts which are stiff enough to stand the compression without bending under it. It does seem to-day that webs in hollow masts have the balance of advantage, and they are probably best formed by thickening the walls, as in *Verona*'s mast, rather than by fully solid portions.

It will be apparent that the crucial parts of a hollow mast are the glued joints. Originally they were made with the old-fashioned hot glues which were soluble in water. For many years the casein powder glue has been used, which is strongly water resisting but not absolutely waterproof. It has proved very effective for masts, and if kept protected will maintain its strength for long periods. To-day one of the phenol-formaldehide glues is generally used and completely waterproof joints are assured; though there are firms of great repute which continue to glue hollow masts with casein.

A number of scarphs may be worked in the length of a mast; there may be five or more separate pieces of timber in each wall of a big spar constructed as in *Fig. 18*, and in most masts there will be two, the joints being made with long scarphs (Plate 4). There is a tradition that the scarphs in staves should not fall opposite one another, but with the glues now available, which make the joints as strong as the wood, this precaution seems hardly necessary.

Light Alloy Masts.—The advantages of alloy masts are smaller weight and windage together with greater strength, whilst the difficulty to-day of getting good, straight-grained spruce, especially for big masts, is a further encouragement for the use of alloy. The 75-ft. spruce mast of the Sparkman & Stephens designed *Gesture* weighed $12\frac{1}{2}$ lb. per foot. The aluminium with which it was replaced 10 lb. per foot. In shorter masts the saving in weight may not be so great, but the proportionate increase in strength over wood will be more, and the staying problem will be simplified. This will be apparent from the 6-Metre masts shown in *Fig. 19*. The class limitation on mast weight necessitates that alloy masts shall be no lighter than those of spruce. The simplification in staying which the greater strength of the alloy allows is evident in comparing *Circe* with *Firecracker*. *Nimrod IV*, a 27-ft. waterline sloop by Sparkman & Stephens, has a 42-ft. aluminium mast carrying a masthead rig; there are no runners and only one set of spreaders. When there is no rule governing mast weight, it is profitable to lighten the mast and accept the more complicated staying; though in the cruiser it may sometimes pay to have the strength in the mast itself, and to use simple and easily tended standing rigging. It depends partly on the beam, and *Nimrod IV* has a length beam ratio of only 2.67.

But the general belief that a light alloy mast will inevitably be stiff and amenable to simplified staying is perhaps too hopeful. This was suggested to me some years ago, at a time when I was being particularly enthusiastic about alloy masts, and was gently asked to repeat what I had said after studying the behaviour of one large example of the type. The opportunity did not occur. The mast in question had folded up first. And subsequently I have seen other alloy masts behave in ways which cannot be called stiff. British 6-Metres have had alloy masts rolled from a flat plate of alloy, and extruded, and these have carried only one spreader, but they have needed both jumpers and standing backstay.

There are also alloy masts of exceptional strength. The difference between the good and the bad must lie in details of design; on the exact alloy used; on the gauge; on the treatment of the alloy in the process of forming the mast; on the internal structure of the spar. All these are hidden engineering details, but they make alloy masts as different from one another as wooden masts of various designs and scantlings may be. The best alloy masts can be very good; but it does seem that we must beware of simplifying the staying simply because alloy is used. It is apparently possible in U.S.A. to produce alloy

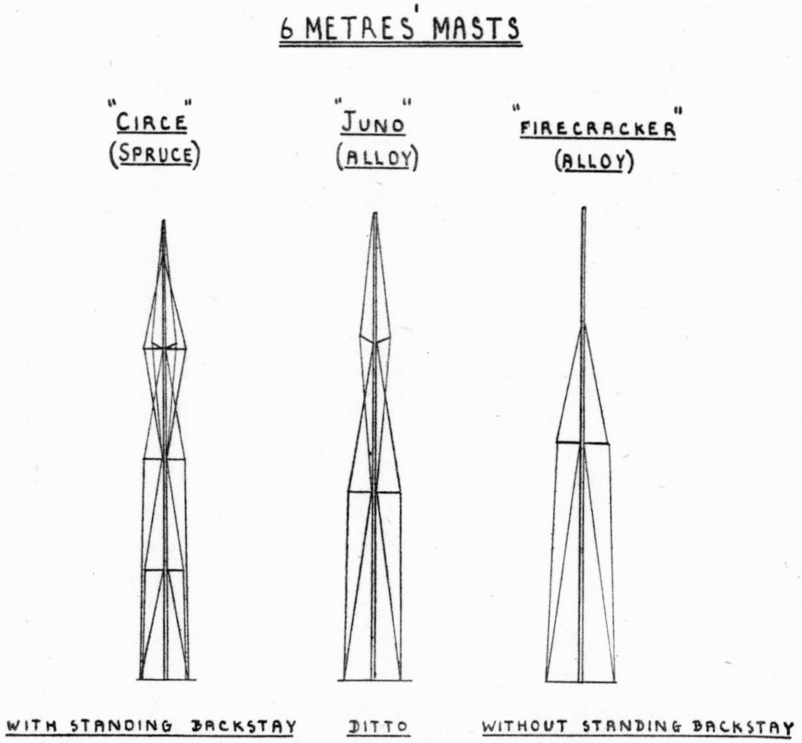

6 METRES' MASTS

"CIRCE" (SPRUCE)   "JUNO" (ALLOY)   "FIRECRACKER" (ALLOY)

WITH STANDING BACKSTAY   DITTO   WITHOUT STANDING BACKSTAY

Figure 19

masts for 6-Metres which will stand with less rigging than our own; yet from the point of view of the rigging stresses which they set up, we may regard all boats of this class as identical. The difference lies in the strength of their apparently similar light alloy masts.

Metal masts may be built up from a number of separate plates, screwed and riveted together; they may be made from extruded sections; and thirdly, in the smallest sizes, they may be formed from a single sheet of alloy folded to the required section. The latter is the method used in the construction of the National Firefly and Swordfish dinghy masts, and since the firm producing them is able to supply these two masts separately, and to a designer's specified length, a range of alloy dinghy masts is now available. In the U.S.A. extruded sections are on the market which are suitable for dinghies and small craft. The small extruded masts are about 50 per cent heavier than the English folded ones, but are smaller in section. In view of the ease with which aluminium alloys are extruded, this sort of mast has a lively future.

Fig. 20 shows the hiduminium mast designed and built by Camper & Nicholsons for the Royal Artillery Club's *St. Barbara*. The mast is 69 ft. 3 in. in length and of an oval section, having major and minor diameters of 10½ in. and 7¾ in. It was designed to carry

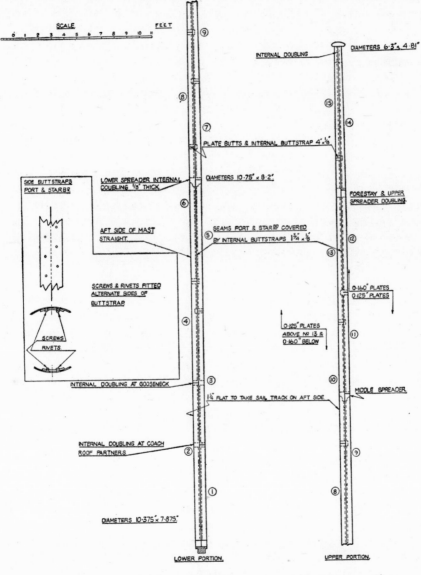

Figure 20.—*St. Barbara*'s hiduminium mast.

a masthead rig, and there were three spreaders. The plating of the mast is 0.16 in. up to the middle spreader, and 0.125 in. above, and the taper starts from this spreader, which is 35 ft. 3 in. above the step. Below the spreader the mast is parallel sided.

The shape of the mast at any section is formed by two plates each rolled to the half section of an oval and butted at the sides of the mast, internal hiduminium butt straps 1¾ in. by 0.125 in. covering these two longitudinal butts internally, and running from head to heel of the mast. There are altogether fourteen plates in the length of the mast, seven forming the fore side and seven the aft side, and the transverse butts of these plates are staggered along the length, those in the fore side plating falling between the aft plate butts. The butts are covered with internal straps 4 in. by 0.125 in. which extend rather more than half round the mast, thus overlapping the butts slightly.

There are many other interesting points of building technique revealed by the plan. It will be seen that the longitudinal butt straps, running up each side of the mast, are fastened to the plating by cadmium-plated steel screws, on one side of each butt, and by rivets on the other. The method of fastening alternates from side to side. Thus, in the two lowest plates of the mast, the plate forming the fore side of the mast, and extending 12 ft. 3 in. above the heel, has the screws to starboard and the rivets to port; in the fore side plate above this one the fastenings are reversed. On the corresponding plates forming the after side, the lowest, which extends 7 ft. 6 in. above the heel, has the screws to port and the rivets to starboard, and the plate above has the reverse.

The use of screws on one side of the butt strap and rivets on the other is due to the difficulty of blind riveting. It will be apparent that the head of a rivet has to be held firmly whilst the point is hammered flat. The length of the plates forming the mast varies between 12 ft. 3 in. and 7 ft. 6 in., and it would not be practicable to hold the head of a rivet which is 7 ft. 6 in. from the end of the tube. The butt strap is therefore riveted on one edge of the plate forming a side of the mast before the plate forming the other is in place. The second plate, with the butt strap riveted to its other side, is then placed to close the oval, and the screws inserted in the butt straps on either side. Thus, in building the mast, the half oval forming the lowest forward half of the mast would have the butt strap riveted to its starboard side. The corresponding aft plate would have the butt strap riveted to its port side. The two halves would then be placed together, and the screws inserted to port and starboard respectively. Plates would then be added forward and aft alternatively until the mast is completed.

At the tapering part of the mast, the flat plates, which are rolled to form the half ovals, are cut and tapered prior to the rolling.

At points along the mast there are doublings to take the stresses of the various fittings. At the heel there is an external doubling 6 in. deep by 0.125 in. thick, riveted to the mast, and internally at the top of this doubling there is a steel angle bar riveted through both mast shell and doubling. This takes the pressure on the spruce plug which forms the mast heel. There are internal doublings at the levels of the coach-roof, gooseneck, and at the spreaders and forestay attachments. These doublings are inserted as the mast is assembled, and the plates are arranged so that a butt in either the forward or aft mast plating falls under the doubling, which then serves also as a butt strap. And, as in the longitudinal doubling on either side of the mast, one side of each doubling is riveted, and the other (upper) side is always screwed.

The above are the main features of large alloy mast construction, and it may be seen that skilful design and workmanship are needed. The work would be greatly simplified were the welding of alloys sufficiently advanced to replace the riveting and screwing at present necessary. The latter work makes an alloy spar more expensive than one built of spruce. Owing to electrolytic action all steel work in contact with the alloy must be cadmium-plated. It will be seen that steel screws are used, this being because of the softness of the alloy.

The built-up metal mast is usually not practicable in the smaller sizes, and the future lies in extruded sections which obviate the rolling and fastening of separate plates, and all the complications involved in the construction of such a mast as *St. Barbara*'s. But specially produced extruded sections are expensive still, and the price becomes reasonable only when a number of masts are being made to the same design. It seems likely that there will soon be available a large variety of standard extruded sections suitable for yachts' masts, including the big sizes, and the wooden mast will become out-dated.

A start has been made with the masts of the R.N.S.A. 24-ft. offshore class, which are aluminium alloy of a pear-shaped section designed by Charles Nicholson and John Illingworth. The same mast is used in the Nicholson *Phoenix II* prototype, and it would be equally suitable for many other yachts. When more sections become available, a designer will have a considerable range from which to choose.

The Twenty-fours' masts are of the same section from head to heel. It would have been possible to make the masts out of two lengths of tube, but actually there are three, the joints being at the two sets of spreaders. Here the sections are butted, there being internal butt straps, as in the *St. Barbara*'s mast, and the straps are riveted to the lower section and screwed to the upper in each case (*Fig. 21*). There is also a doubling from the heel of the mast to 3 ft. 6 in. above the deck. The masts are of slightly under one-eighth of an inch in thickness, and there is no saving in weight over spruce ones, though there is a gain in stiffness. The masts might have been of less thickness and still of adequate strength when the saving in weight would have been about 12 per cent over a spruce spar.

It is possible, though of slight advantage, to obtain taper in extruded sections by cutting a deep, narrow V out of the top section of a mast, and welding it together again. The result is a lowering of the C.G. and an improvement in appearance. A less expensive way of getting taper is to make the top section of a mast in wood, socketing it into the alloy section and fastening it under one of the mast fittings. Some years before the war, racing models were sometimes fitted with alloy masts the taper of which was made by using progressively smaller

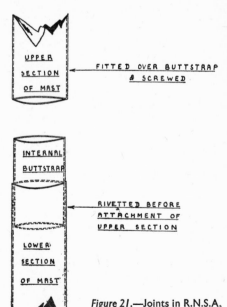

Figure 21.—Joints in R.N.S.A. 24-ft. class alloy extruded masts.

G

tubes, slipped inside each other. By this means the C.G. of a mast is drawn well below its mid-point.

Gesture's mast, which is 6 ft. longer than *St. Barbara*'s, was built similarly to those for the R.N.S.A. class, in three sections riveted over internal doublings. The top section was tapered by cutting from it two V strips 11 ft. deep. The extrusions from which the mast was made were circular in section, subsequently being rolled to the elliptical shape, and the finished dimensions were $11\frac{7}{16} \times 6\frac{7}{16} \times 0.22$ in. It will be seen that the spar has a greater fore and aft scantling than *St. Barbara*'s, and is narrow athwartships. The thickness of the alloy is also about 27 per cent more than that of *St. Barbara*'s lower sections, and nearly 50 per cent more than the upper part, *Gesture*'s mast being of constant thickness throughout. Against this greater thickness must be set the absence of the laps and many butt straps in the Royal Artillery's yacht's mast, which adds to its strength and weight. On the balance the two masts are probably not markedly different in weight or strength, and the extruded mast removes the troubles which occur with rivet and screw connections when a built-up mast deflects under compression.

6

ROPE

Wire Rope.—Makers of wire rope may have seventy or more different constructions of rope to offer, each with certain virtues and better than any other for its particular purpose. This fact may serve as a caution to those for whom all wire rope is much the same and, like Italian hemp or Manilla, differentiated mainly by the size. The situation is actually less complicated than may be suggested above, for of the seventy or so constructions only about a dozen are useful in yachts; but still there is a considerable freedom of choice when ordering wire for rigging. Various constructions of wire rope which may be found in the standing and running rigging of yachts are shown in *Fig. 22*.

The most important variables in construction are the number of individual wires in each strand, the number of strands in the rope, and the number of hemp cores. Wire ropes may be designated by means of three numerals, the first giving the number of strands, the second the number of wires in a strand, the third the number of cores. When no hemp is embodied in the rope the third numeral may be omitted. Thus a $6 \times 7 \times 1$ steel rope consists of six strands each of severn wires laid up round a central hempen core; a 1×19 rope is a single strand rope composed of nineteen wires; a $6 \times 18 \times 1$ rope has six strands of eighteen wires laid up round a central hempen core; whilst in a $6 \times 18 \times 7$ rope there is a hemp core in each of the strands as well as in the complete rope.

Flexibility in a rope is achieved by making the individual wires composing its strands small—that is, by increasing the number of wires in a rope of given size—and by introducing the hempen cores into the rope and strands. In general ,the more numerous the individual wires in a strand the more flexible a rope will be; a $6 \times 27 \times 1$ rope is more flexible than a $6 \times 19 \times 1$ rope and less so than a $6 \times 37 \times 1$ rope. But $6 \times 18 \times 7$ is more flexible than any of these, in spite of the fewer wires in each strand, because each strand has a hempen heart, and $6 \times 15 \times 7$ is the most flexible of all, the individual wires being very small and the bulk of each strand being hemp. Indeed, this particular rope is virtually a hempen one lightly encased in steel.

The small wires and the hempen cores of flexible ropes reduce their strengths, make them more liable, as we shall see, to rust and corrosion, and produce a greater amount of stretch under load. Flexibility is thus antagonistic to many of the other important qualities of a rope, and no piece of rigging should be made of more flexible rope than its purpose demands; $6 \times 24 \times 7$ flexible rope, for example, has about 80 per cent of the strength of $6 \times 7 \times 1$ and about five times the amount of stretch. The former would serve for running rigging, the latter for standing.

Drawing is the process by which the initially oversize wires, or thin rods, are reduced, by squeezing and elongation, to their final diameter, which is achieved to an accuracy of less than one thousandth of an inch. The rods are drawn cold, but are subject to heat treatment at various stages of the process. In ordinary rope the individual wires are then twisted up into a strand. In pre-formed rope each wire is given, before being laid up, the helical of spiral curve which it eventually assumes in the strand. This results in a rope which is easier to splice and handle, whilst internal stresses in the rope are relieved and an even loading in the wires and strands is more likely to be assured.

Wire rope may be made of steel, galvanised, which is most commonly used in English yachts, or of various alloys such as phosphor bronze, monel, nickel, or stainless steel, the latter providing, when of the best quality, the finest rigging at present available. The other alloys are now little used in yachts' rigging.

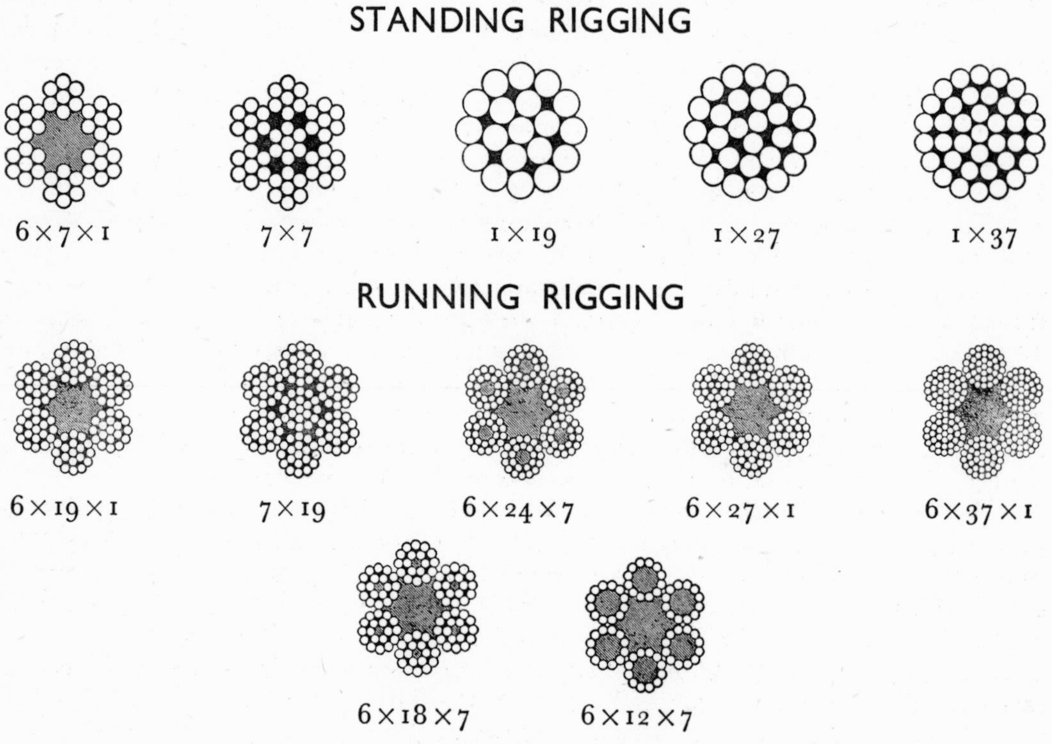

STANDING RIGGING

6 × 7 × 1   7 × 7   1 × 19   1 × 27   1 × 37

RUNNING RIGGING

6 × 19 × 1   7 × 19   6 × 24 × 7   6 × 27 × 1   6 × 37 × 1

6 × 18 × 7   6 × 12 × 7

Figure 22.—Construction of Wire Rope.

Steel rope rusts. The protection against this provided by galvanising consists of a coating of zinc on each wire of the rope, and the efficacy of the protection depends largely on the thickness of the zinc coating. The zinc protects; but it adds only insignificantly to the strength of a rope, though appreciably so to its weight, zinc being heavier than steel. In certain ropes the zinc may account for one-fifth of the total weight, and thus an argument in favour of stainless steel for rigging is immediately apparent. The amount of zinc covering required increases with the number of individual wires in a rope, the surface area of many small wires being greater than that of a fewer larger ones making strands of equal size. Thus it is possible, without reducing unduly the strength-weight ratio, to protect adequately the nineteen wires of 1 × 19 rope, and protection becomes progressively more difficult with the forty-nine wires of 7 × 7 rope, the 114 of 6 × 19 rope, and the 168 of 7 × 24 rope.

In all good wire rope the strands are galvanised separately before being formed into the rope; though it is believed that many manufacturers do not in fact do this. Three processes of galvanising rope are in general used:

(*a*) Hot bath galvanising.

(*b*) Hot bath galvanising followed by drawing.

(*c*) Electrolytic galvanising.

Many factors, including the price of zinc at nearly £200 per ton, accounted for the very poor quality of galvanised wire rope in the years following the war. Manufacturers tended to economise on the amount of zinc deposited and to reduce it to a minimum. Even to-day galvanised wire rope may be found to be unsatisfactory. In a recent yacht from a good yard and built under careful supervision the standing rigging was heavily rusted after a few months in commission. It may have been mainly surface rust, but its existence, and so extensively, showed an equally extensive absence of zinc protection.

In the U.S.A. wire of stainless steel—a non-corroding alloy of steel with nickle and chromium—is generally used in the rigging of yachts and even in the smallest craft. Its chief advantages over galvanised wire are its long life and usually a slightly greater strength; its disadvantage the very high price. In England a few yachts have stainless rigging; a majority, including the products of first-class yards, do not. In this country it is possible to have three sets of galvanised rigging, and have money to spare for the turning of the splices and the fitting, for the price of one set of stainless.

The life of stainless steel rope used for standing rigging is about ten years. Though considerable improvements have been made in the processing of stainless steel during recent years, it is slightly more subject to failure through fatigue than galvanised steel, and English rope of this type seems to be of little use at the moment for running rigging. A piece of rigging for which stainless steel wire obviously suggests itself is the whip of each runner backstay, where the constant running under stress over blocks destroys the galvanising in a few weeks. The length of rope needed here is not great so that the extra expense of stainless wire is inconsiderable. But it will be found that with English stainless steel wire rope the individual wires start breaking almost as soon as galvanised wire would start rusting.

I believe that this poorness of quality is due to a Ministry of Supply order which forbids the use of more than a low percentage of nickel in wire used for yachts' rigging. So, for English yachtsmen, it would seem that they must either find a way of obtaining American stainless steel rope, or use galvanised rope for running rigging.

Rope for Standing Rigging.—For standing rigging the important requirements are strength, freedom from stretch, and resistance to rust and corrosion. At the moment 1 × 19 rope, composed of nineteen single wires laid up together, stands at the top of the list, having elbowed the older 7 × 7 construction into second place. It is a superior product to the 7 × 7 rope, which together with the still widely used 6 × 7, are the most commonly found in English yachts. In the U.S.A. 1 × 19 has become the almost certain choice. This rope approaches the strength and freedom from stretch of solid rod. Being composed of nineteen individual wires, instead of forty-nine in the case of 7 × 7, each wire is of greater size for a given diameter of rope, less liable to damage, and better able if galvanised to hold its coating of zinc.

A certain number of first-class yachts have appeared in recent years with standing rigging of 1 × 27 or 1 × 37 rope. These, with their smaller individual wires, are less resistant to rust and corrosion than 1 × 19, and they stretch more, whilst their slightly greater flexibility is not needed. In general, fewer rather than more individual wires are needed in rope which is to fulfil our three requirements for standing rigging, and it seems possible that a rope such as 1 × 7, composed of a central wire with six others laid round it, would be most suitable, though it has not been adopted up to date.

Rope of 7 × 7 construction is second only to 1 × 19 rope for our purpose. It is slightly more flexible than the latter and has a little more stretch. It is much superior to the much-used 6 × 7 as a result of having a heart strand of wire, which is similar to the other six strands which are laid around it. This reduces the stretch in the rope and also its resistance to compression; 6 × 7 rope has the same strands of seven wires each, but in place of the seventh heart strand there is a hemp core. This is the older design of rope and is still perhaps the most commonly used in spite of its grave defects. The hemp core may contain a preservative against the internal corrosion of the wires, but this advantage is nullified by the tendency of the soft core to collapse, allowing internal chafing of the wires and early fatigue; also, of course, serious stretch. Furthermore, the hemp heart in time dries and hardens, and eventually absorbs water and rots.

Wire for Running Rigging.—The most commonly used construction in England to-day is the 6 × 19 × 1 wire, which serves for halyards, sheets, topping lifts, boom guys, clew outhauls, reef pendants, and a variety of other purposes. This wire consists of six strands each composed of nineteen wires and laid up round a central hempen core or heart— hence 6 × 19 × 1. This is a construction of wire which strikes a good balance for its purpose between flexibility and the opposed qualities of strength and resistance to stretch and corrosion. With only nineteen wires in the strand each is individually big enough to carry a reasonably thick covering of zinc protection in a galvanised rope. Or at least it has a better chance of doing so.

In the U.S.A. 6 × 19 × 1 rope is giving way to 7 × 19 construction, in which the hempen heart is replaced by a wire strand similar to the six outer ones. This is analogous to the use of 7 × 7 standing rigging in place of the older 6 × 7 wire with its hempen core. The advantage claimed for 7 × 19 flexible wire rope is that the wire prevents the crushing and deformation of the rope which the hempen core of the 6 × 19 × 1 rope is unable to resist. Messrs. Merriman are strong in their recommendation of 7 × 19 wire for all running rigging, and what this knowledgeable firm says would appear to carry much influence amongst American yachtsmen. But there are those who disagree. They claim, and to this extent are certainly right, that in yachts wire is made to run over sheaves (and sometimes winches also) of much smaller diameter than should be used for the size of the wire. The hemp heart of the 6 × 19 × 1 rope allows it to become oval at the turn and hence to reduce the stresses in its outer wires; the 7 × 19 variety, remaining circular, puts high stresses in the outer wires, which eventually snap.

There is perhaps something to be said for both sides in this argument. Rope in which individual wires have snapped can become dangerous to handle, especially if the wire is not preformed, when the broken wires become like hedgehog bristles; and it is obviously weakened. In order to avoid this it may be better to use a wire which becomes oval under stress, and to put up with the internal abrasion and eventual fatigue which must result from it. We may say that where the sheave size has, for some reason, to be undesirably low, $6 \times 19 \times 1$ rope may be the better one to use, though it should be kept under constant surveillance for signs of permanent deformation. When exceptional flexibility is needed 6×24 wire may be used, this being of two types, the first $6 \times 24 \times 1$ having one central hemp core, the second $6 \times 24 \times 7$ having in addition a hemp core in each strand; 6×37 is another very flexible rope used for running rigging. With these more flexible wires the price is paid in strength and durability. It may be considered a payment well worth while when attempting to coil down steel wire sheets or halyards, which can be the most exasperating pieces of gear in a ship, and definitely dangerous ones too when a stiff sheet jumps a winch.

Sheave Diameters.—The sizes of sheaves specified by makers as ideal for the various diameters of rope are usually far above anything that can be adopted in yachts. For example, thirty times the rope diameter is considered to be a reasonable sheave diameter for $6 \times 19 \times 1$ wire. As an absolute minimum we may accept sixteen times the diameter, or eighteen times the diameter for 7×19 wire. Using a $6 \times 37 \times 1$ wire a minimum sheave size of fourteen times the rope's diameter may be adopted.

Swaged Ends for Standing Rigging.—The use of swaged sockets instead of splices for the ends of standing rigging is now more general than it used to be. If the socket, into which the wire is fixed by the swaging process, has the same strength as the wire the swaging seems to give 100 per cent strength instead of the 80 per cent of the ordinary splice. Since standing rigging is rarely stressed up to 80 per cent of its ultimate strength owing, amongst other things, to the stretch which would result, this is a safeguard rather than a material advantage. But the swaged end is an altogether neater arrangement; also, with the excellent 1×19 rope, splicing is not only difficult but dangerous owing to the tendency of the big individual wires to break. The swaged end is also easier to look after and probably less liable to deteriorate.

We say " probably " because even swaged ends are capable of deterioration and must be watched. In the U.S.A., where there is a wider experience of swaged ends, it was once considered essential to discard a fitting as soon as small hair-line cracks appeared on the barrel of the socket. These cracks start inside the socket, and it was assumed that once they had become visible externally the fitting was too seriously weakened to be retained.

Laboratory tests more recently have revealed that the small cracks are not as serious as they might appear. Of the fittings tested, all of which had given eleven years' service and showed one or more cracks, only two failed and both of these were severely cracked in several places.

The nature of the cracks, which may appear after a few years' service, are shown in the diagram. One of the best known makers of rigging wire in England, who has supplied a great many outfits with swaged ends in recent years, has told me that he has not heard of any trouble with the sockets; but he added that with modern galvanised rigging one set was not expected to last many years. And this obviously reduces the demands on the sockets. There seem good reasons for protecting the swaged ends. It has been suggested that they should be dipped in hot tallow or paraffin wax; and even if without this treatment it is a good practice to serve them like splices with insulating tape.

Several points of maintenance may be noted. Swages, like splices, appear to be affected by spray and salt; hence the fittings at the lower ends of the rigging are more likely to deteriorate than those on the mast. Sunlight also encourages cracks.

Rod Rigging.—Rod rigging, which seems to have so many advantages, and towards which all developments in non-flexible wire rope have tended, still remains a rarity, and for the present seems likely to remain so for general purposes. Some of the J-class used rod; *Astra* also has it and a number of the Sixes—*Kyria*, for example, and *Goose*. The 5.5-Metre *Yeoman* (Plate 3), designed by Charles A. Nicholson and built by Messrs. Camper and Nicholsons, appeared in 1952 with rod rigging. *Yolaine*, of the same class and designed by David Boyd, came out a year later with wire rigging. In the Herreshoff Islander class, a type of fast dayboat built in England by Messrs. Port Hamble on a semi-massed-produced basis, rod rigging was fitted. In the U.S.A. cruisers have had rod rigging which has given service without failure for thirteen years and more. But, in general, opinion is still against it for craft other than inshore racers, and even here we see that opinions are divided.

Rod has the advantage, for a given strength, of lightness, very little stretch, and a small diameter. The size of the rods may be varied in the mast's panels in accordance with the loads, the top panels having very light rod; but the same effect may be achieved by linked rigging when using wire. Many of the Scandinavian 5.5-Metres use rod rigging of $\frac{1}{8}$ in. diameter. In so small a size as this the rod is essentially simply a solid drawn wire, a single strand of a larger wire rope. The end fittings, which become complicated and expensive with larger rods, are simplified, the thin rods being simply bent round the thimble and secured.

Failures in rod rigging are caused by treating it like wire and setting it up too taut. Owing to the negligible stretch of rod it is only necessary to set up the rigging so that there is no slack in it. There is, for obvious reasons, no justification for the use of streamlined rods, which have been fitted to yachts in the past, and rods of round section should be used. To retain the strength in the screw threaded portions of the rod, the ends have to be thickened, or upset; or in some cases manufacturers roll or draw the rod between the threaded ends to a smaller diameter.

With about 15 per cent greater strength for a given diameter than wire, rod rigging gives an opportunity of saving considerable weight and windage aloft, and in the U.S.A. there are even cruising yachtsmen who regard it as safer, and in the long run more economical, than wire. Designers on the whole remain indifferent to it even for small boats, fitting it at the owner's wish more often than their own. Messrs. Merriman, the American specialists in yacht fittings and rigging, are not in favour of it. A disadvantage of rods is their frailty. They are easily bent. Even with perfect maintenance there is danger of failure from the fatigue engendered in the rods by their strumming in the wind, and from vibrations transferred through the hull; whilst the stresses transmitted by the relatively inflexible rod to the terminal fittings, encourage failure in these. One may accept the risk of failure inshore but not offshore.

Fibre Rope.—" The other day," Hilaire Belloc once wrote, " as I was sailing down-channel at dawn I contemplated a piece of rope (which was my only companion) and considered how many things attach to it, and of what sort these were."

Rope has a very long history and may even be classed with the wheel as one of man's fundamental inventions. Until recently it was at the root of seafaring. And still to-day it is undergoing technical improvements, though it offers fewer complications in construction than wire, and presents a less confusing range of choices when used for the various rigging purposes for which it is still the most suitable material. These purposes are, however, becoming fewer. There are yachts to-day in which rope is used only for the mainsheet, the tails of halyards and headsail sheets, and a few odd purchases.

Most of the rope in use to-day still consists basically of a vegetable fibre, initially in short lengths, which is delivered to the manufacturer in bales. The fibres come from plants, the best known of which grow in the Philippines and make the various grades of Manilla rope, and in Piedmont, which is the source of Italian hemp. The fibres of the Sisal plant, which grows in East Africa, Mexico, and in Japan, are also used to make hemp rope.

The fibres are combed out by mechanical means, their high internal friction, which prevents slipping between the fibres, allowing them to be run into a long ribbon of the substance. From this the yarns are twisted or spun, which again increases the friction, and these are spun into strands, which in turn are laid up into rope. The various processes of twisting, the twist being reversed at each stage in the progress towards the finished rope, produces a material, which may be of great length and strength, out of short fibres.

The rope used on board to-day is mainly three stranded, or hawser laid, having the strands laid right-handed, on from left to right, and such a rope is always coiled clockwise. It is customary in Britain, and also the old tradition of the sea, to designate rope size by the circumference. In the U.S.A. amongst yachtsmen the habit has grown up of using the more logical, because more readily visualised, dimension of diameter.

Manilla is a golden rope which appears in many qualities, the finest being yacht quality: Italian hemp, which is greyer in colour, is a stronger rope, except in large sizes, lasts slightly better than Manilla, and is especially pleasant to handle. It serves well for large mainsheets, but it is expensive. Lightly tarred Italian hemp is often used. The tarring weakens the rope slightly, but increases its resistance to rot; and for this same purpose American manufacturers lubricate Manilla with an oil which increases its resistance to the absorption of water. Sisal rope is of a poorer quality hemp, originally very white in colour, weaker than Manilla and Italian hemp, and generally of unpleasing appearance owing to its roughness.

Cotton rope is rarely used in Britain, though more commonly so in the U.S.A., and in Europe it is sometimes adopted for such important parts of the rigging as the mainsheet —even in large yachts. In such cases tarred cotton is generally used. It is a relatively weak rope, and becomes very hard and difficult to handle when wet. It is liable to rot, and is not trustworthy for important work.

Linen rope was once common in English yachts, and it earned a high reputation all over the world. Its strength, in normal yacht sizes, is about 20 per cent greater than Manilla. It is now popular in the U.S.A., when its high price can be afforded, but it is rarely found in British yachts.

Rope of synthetic fibre, such as nylon, is the latest arrival in the field of rope making. Nylon has many advantages which make it superior to rope of vegetable fibre; but it also has weaknesses which, apart from its high price, militate against it. It has about 75 per cent more strength than Manilla; it runs freely and is easy to handle when wet; and it is free from any tendency to develop rot or mildew. These are high virtues to set against its considerable stretch under load—more than twice that of Manilla and three times that of Italian hemp. It is thus unsuitable to take the load of halyards, and it is even considered by some that it upsets the trim of sails when used for sheets. It seems to have another disadvantage which is rarely noted—a low resistance to abrasion. I understand that for this reason mountain climbers will not use this rope in spite of its other obvious qualities. Certainly if a nylon sheet develops an unfair lead in a deck bonnet or other fitting, and then comes under a heavy load, it appears to strand more readily than one of vegetable fibre. Such accidents, which a fibre one would probably survive, destroy a nylon rope, and with great ease.

Other synthetic fibre ropes are appearing on the market. One of these, known in the U.S.A. as dacron, apparently has the best qualities of nylon but without the latter's stretch. It may be expected that from a material such as this an almost perfect rope for yacht work may soon be evolved.

7

BLOCKS AND TACKLES

Tackles.—These are used to increase the power which may be obtained by hauling on a line, or to change the direction of the pull. Historically blocks and tackles are the basis of rigging; they alone having allowed the relatively puny strength of men to control the forces engendered by the wind in large areas of canvas. In the modern yacht they are less used than in any previous craft, having been replaced to a considerable extent by winches and levers, which are simply another and more compact method of obtaining a mechanical advantage. Blocks of many different designs are still used in yachts to alter the direction of pull on a wire or rope. The principal tackle is the mainsheet, though others may be used in halyards, downhauls and outhauls, topping lifts, and sheets. Sometimes a winch and tackle will be used together, as on the mainsheet; in other places the winch will often be the substitute for the tackle. We may say that the more expensively rigged a yacht is, the more numerous will be the winches found on board, the fewer will be the tackles, and the easier the boat will be to handle.

The power of a tackle is governed firstly by the number of parts of rope led to or from or attached to the moving block of the tackle, and secondly on the friction in the blocks. When a line is rove through a single fixed block, as for example in the deck sheet lead for a headsail, no power is gained from the block, and a certain amount is lost due to friction in the block. This is the arrangement shown in *Fig. 23 (a)*, which is also the same as a single portmain halyard passing over a masthead sheave, or indeed of any halyard passing over a mast sheave. To lift the weight W an effort of W + F must be applied to the fall of the rope, F being equal to the friction which has to be overcome.

The friction is largely governed by the number of sheaves in the blocks of the tackle and by the amount of weight which has to be lifted, and an approximate allowance which may be made is $\dfrac{W}{10}$ for each sheave. In the case of *Fig. 23 (a)*, this arrangement being known as a single whip, the effort which must be applied to lift W is therefore $W + \dfrac{W}{10}$.

Certain other facts should be noted about this single whip, which is found in so many places in a yacht. The power gained is not influenced in this (or in any other) tackle by the sizes of the sheaves. The amount of the friction, however, is reduced by increasing their sizes. Though no power is gained, the load on the pin of the sheave and in the attachment of the block is equal to $2W + \dfrac{W}{10}$. That is, it is almost double the actual pull in the hauling part of the tackle. This fact will be obvious when it is realised that the block carries not only the load of W which is in the part of the rope entering the block, but also of $W + \dfrac{W}{10}$ which is in the part leaving it. The implications of this may be considered, for example, in the case of the block of a Genoa sheet lead. The weight in the sheet of a large Genoa as the wind hardens is very great; the block attachment may carry about double this weight, which in turn is transferred to the deck track carrying the block. Hence the periodical failure of these blocks, even when made by the best manufacturers, and the lifting and buckling of apparently well-fastened lengths of track.

Of course, in the case of sheet leads on deck the stresses in the block and fitting are effected by the angles of the lead into and out of the block, and the wide angle which the two parts of the sheet make at the block in some layouts reduces the stresses in the block. But often, when the sheet is led forward to a winch the layout is essentially that of the whip in *Fig. 23 (a)*. A main halyard also follows, and more closely, the pattern of the whip. Hence the shear stresses in the pin of the masthead sheave, and the compression in the mast due to the halyard, is about twice the weight in the fall of the halyard. In many yachts, from J-class to 6-Metre boats, devices have been fitted at the masthead which lock the headboard in position when the sail has been fully hoisted. The sail is, in effect, hung aloft on a hook, and once hoisted there is no weight in its halyard. The result is a halving of the compressive load due to the halyard.

Other simple forms of purchase commonly used in yachts are shown in *Fig. 23*. The double whip comprises two single blocks with the fall led from the fixed block (*Fig. 23 (b)*). It will be seen that there are two parts in the moving (lower) block. Neglecting friction this gives a power of two; there are two sheaves producing friction, at $\frac{W}{10}$ per sheave, of $\frac{W}{5}$, so that the total load to be lifted will be $W + \frac{W}{5}$, and the effort needed will be $\dfrac{W + \frac{W}{5}}{2}$, or 3/5 W.

It should be noted that we have here neglected one element in the calculation, and that is the weight of the block and rope, which for strict accuracy should be added, like the friction, to W. We may thus establish the simple formula

$$E = \frac{W + S\frac{(L)}{(10)} + B}{N}$$ where E = effort, W = load or weight, S = number of

sheaves in the blocks of the purchase, B = the weight of the moving block and rope, N = number of parts in or attached to the moving block. More simply, most people will consider it good enough to find an approximate answer by simply dividing the weight or load by N, and make a rough allowance for the losses in power.

If the fall of the double whip purchase is led from the moving block (*Fig. 23 (c)*) the power of the tackle is increased from two to three, but as the blocks remain the same the friction is not increased. Neglecting the weight of the block and rope, the load is again $W + \frac{W}{5}$, so that the effort needed is $\dfrac{W + \frac{W}{5}}{3} = 2/5$ W. An effort of 60 lb. will therefore move 150 lb. This form of tackle would be suitable for the mainsail outhaul in many yachts, though more power would be needed in large craft.

The same power is obtained in the luff tackle (*d*) consisting of a double and single

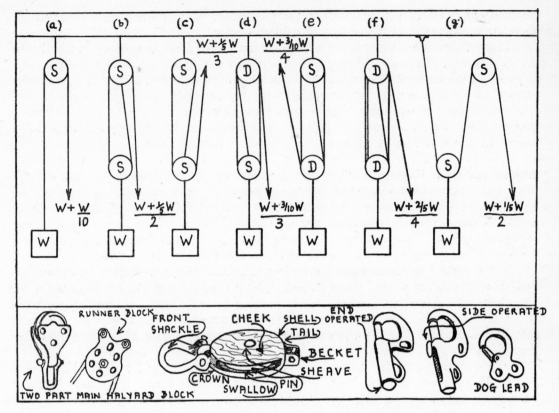

Figure 23.—Power of various purchases. Parts of blocks and types of headsail hanks.

block with the fall led from the double block, but friction is increased by the addition of one sheave to 3/10 W. A power of four is obtained if the double block is the moving one (*e*). In the first case, and again neglecting the weight of the tackle, the effort needed is

$$\frac{W + 3/10\ W}{3} = \frac{13}{30}\ W, \text{ and in the second } \frac{W + 3/10\ W}{4} = \frac{13}{40}\ W.$$

If now two double blocks are used (*f*) the power will be four, or five if the fall is led from the moving block (excluding friction in both cases). In the more complicated tackles, and especially those involving double blocks, friction may be higher than the theoretical allowance, for in practice fair leads are not always obtainable, and the blocks tend to twist, producing high friction between the parts of the tackle.

At one time much use was made of two tackles working in combination, when very high power was needed, the second purchase being clapped on to the fall of the first. The total power of such an arrangement—again excluding friction—is equal to the product of the powers of the two separate tackles. If we clap a three-power purchase on to the fall of a four-power purchase a total theoretical power of twelve is gained.

Grab tackles of this sort were used on the J-class boats to increase the power of their six-part mainsheets. To-day the smaller areas of canvas which are handled, and the more extensive use of winches, reduce the importance of compound tackles, which are therefore rarely found in the rigging of modern yachts.

It must always be remembered with purchases (or with winches, or any other device for gaining a mechanical advantage) that with every increase in power there follows a decrease in the speed of operation. A single whip gives no increase in power; a double whip gives a power of two, but compared with a single whip twice the amount of rope has to be hauled through the block when trimming a sheet or hoisting a sail. With a power of four, four times the amount of rope has to be overhauled. Speed of operation is inversely proportional to power.

Blocks and their Fittings.—The traditional woods for making blocks were ash, lignum vitae, and elm, and still to-day ash blocks are in the majority on board yachts (Plate 30 and others). But now many other materials are used for the shells, which may be of malleable iron, steel galvanised or stainless (Plate 6), gunmetal, manganese bronze, and of plastics such as Tufnol, which is linen bonded with synthetic resin. The mainsheet blocks in Plate 19 and the headsail sheet lead block in Plate 25 are of Tufnol.

The names of the various parts of a block are shown in *Fig. 23*. From this it will be seen that the two cheeks and two separating pieces at the crown and tail form the shell. The shells of wooden blocks, which are turned out by craftsmen more quickly than the price of yachts' blocks would suggest, are fastened together by bronze pins. The best metal blocks have shells in one piece, not riveted together, and their proportions differ from those of wood blocks.

The space between the cheeks is the mortice or swallow, and into this the sheave is fitted. This rotates on a fixed pin, between which and the sheave there may be roller bearings to reduce friction. The size of rope to which a block is suited is governed by the width of the mortice and the diameter of the sheave, but as the proportions of ordinary wood blocks are standardised the rope size may be related to the blocks' length. This system, however, cannot be applied to metal blocks or to wooden ones of unusual proportions intended for special purposes.

Formerly wooden blocks were usually plain, having a score in the shell at crown and tail to take a rope or wire strop worked round a thimble. Large blocks, intended to carry heavier loads than the wooden shell might be expected to bear, had internal straps let into grooves in the cheeks. Stropped blocks have now largely given place to ones having a variety of metal fittings, which are usually formed by extensions of an internal strap. The most common fitting is a metal eye at the crown of the block (Plate 30) shaped to carry a shackle, whilst the tail may carry another eye, the becket, to take the eyesplice of the standing part of the wire or rope.

The front of a block is the view obtained when looking into the mortice; the sides are formed by either cheek. The type of fitting on the block is designated by the way in which it holds the shackle in relation to the front and side of the block, and by the way in which the shackle is held (*Fig. 23*). Shackles inserted from the side of the block are side shackles, those from the front, front shackles, and when the eye of the shackle passes through the eye of the block it is called an upset shackle. There are thus four main types of simple block fitting: (i) Front Shackle; (ii) Side Shackle; (iii) Upset Front Shackle; (iv) Upset Side Shackle. Blocks carrying these fittings may be single, double, or treble, and with or without becket. The terms front and side may also be applied on the same principle to fittings other than shackles.

There is now a great range of such fittings designed for various special purposes in the rigging of yachts, and also a number of specialised types of blocks. There are ones with a specially wide mortice in relation to the length of the shell, carrying a sheave suitable for large rope, and these are of use as the deck lead blocks of sheets. Blocks are designed with large diameter sheaves for their size, these being desirable in the purchases of halyards, the rip on the wire being eased. Sheaves scored to take both wire and rope may be fitted. These are needed for such purposes as halyards, when a rope tail may be required to pass the mast block as well as the wire. Sister or fiddle blocks, which are double blocks with the sheaves separated and on different pins, are useful in positions, such as for an outhaul on a boom, where the thickness of a normal double block would be inconvenient (*Fig. 37*).

Of the numerous fittings now embodied on blocks one of the simplest is the swivel eye, an arrangement needed in many parts of the rigging, where a twist might occur with the normal fixed eye. Related to this is the block with a swivel hook. The swivel snap shackle block has now become one of the most ubiquitous fittings. Blocks of this type may be snapped into the sliders of deck tracks and into deck eyebolts for headsail sheet leads. Ideal for this purpose is the snap shackle snatch block (Plate 9) which combines the spring shackle with a hinged top to the block—an elaboration, with a spring mechanism, of the older type of snatch block—allowing sheets to be quickly rove without the need for leading the whole length through the block. Blocks of this sort are expensive, but their wide use suggests their value. The straps and fittings are usually of manganese bronze, and though of considerable strength they sometimes fail. I have seen two carry away, both when in use as lead blocks for a headsail sheet, and both under heavy load. Another type of snatch block, shackled in this case to a deck eyeplate, is shown in Plate 6.

Any block with a swivel or fixed, screw or spring shackle may be attached to a deck eyeplate. A refinement is blocks designed as an integral part of the eyeplate. These are suitable for mainsheet quarter blocks, for blocks at the foot of the mast on deck for halyard purchases, and in other places where the block may conveniently or necessarily remain permanently in position.

The eyeplate may be of various designs, its most important function being to provide a secure fastening through the deck and deck beam or reinforcement. The heavy load carried by such blocks results in their lifting or working in the deck when, as too often is the case, their fastening is inadequate. The plate may be round with four bolts equally spaced round the circumference; they may be diamond-shaped; or they may be rectangular, with only two bolts, a design which may be necessary when the fastenings have to pass through a narrow beam. Sometimes the plate is omitted altogether, the eye carrying the block being forged on a single bolt.

In such fittings as these the strap of the block is worked into an eye fitting permanently and closely into the eye of the deck plate, and a more elaborate fitting is made in which the two eyes are so shaped that the block cannot fall below a certain angle, this preventing fouling of the lead or damage to the decks. The same effect may be achieved by the fitting of a light metal cage round the block (Plate 7).

Blocks, both wood and metal, are made having a permanent attachment to the slides of deck tracks. But as it is convenient to be able to unship the block from the slide, the snap shackle block is superior in this position.

Blocks are also made with a saddle fitting worked into the eye of the block for use in main sheet purchases in which the blocks are slung from boom bridles (Plate 8). Such blocks may also be used in the peak halyards of gaff sails, or in small boats when the mainsheet runs on a bridle instead of a horse. A block is also specially made for the main outhaul and topping lift purchases on booms, where the moving block runs in a track on the boom (Plate 8). This consists of a slide which fits the track and which is screwed to the cheek of the block.

· 8 ·

SHROUDS

WE may define standing rigging as rigging whose function it is to support the mast and carry sails. Running rigging sets or controls the sails. Shrouds, runners, standing backstays are devoted exclusively to the support of the mast; forestays support the mast and usually carry sails as well.

Shrouds provide the athwartship support of the mast, and the lower shrouds also help slightly, under certain conditions, in giving it rigidity fore and aft; though this is primarily the function of other parts of the standing rigging. Shrouds consist of lower shrouds, intermediate shrouds, and masthead shrouds, and together with these we may include jumper stays, which, being angled slightly forward, serve both as shrouds and forestays. Together these wires form the athwartship bracing of the mast (though slight additional help also comes from the runners) and the mast is thus a braced strut, not a cantilever as the airmen think it should be. It is, in fact, an old fashioned contrivance, and by means of certain approximate formulae, combined with a few reasonable assumptions, it can be calculated that the shrouds of an International 14-ft. dinghy reduce the speed of the boat by rather more than a third of a knot in a 10-knot breeze, due to their air resistance. The Vosper–Hasler Lapwing rig has an unstayed mast, and craft having masts unsupported by standing rigging—cantilever masts—have ranged from junks, log canoes, and cat boats, to Scandinavian 22-Sq. Metre racers; but desirable though it may be to eliminate standing rigging we still have with us to-day, and in a pretty intense form, what somebody once called the malady of stays.

Yet we have improved much. A glance at the staying plans of early Bermudian masts, known then not inaptly as Marconi after the wireless masts, will reveal a complete network of wires which has to-day been replaced by altogether cleaner, simpler, yet stronger arrangements. We have also reduced the weight and windage of standing rigging by using stronger wire rope and more efficient rigging attachments, which allow the full strength of the wire to be developed. There is a singular lack of numerical data on the stresses in standing rigging, and this is often commented on by engineers as an example of the yacht designer's empirical approach to his work. Strain gauges have occasionally been used on standing rigging or incorporated in a stay. An example was in the 11-ton *Joliette*, designed by Robert Clark for Mr. F. W. Morgan, which raced across the Atlantic after the Bermuda Race of 1952. The boat was a masthead cutter, and the gauge was worked in with the lower-end attachment of the standing backstay. No detailed record of readings was kept, but the following figures may be offered as examples of those obtained:

Static Load in Standing Backstay	1,800 lb.
Load under normal sailing conditions	2,200 lb.
Load when sailing with rail down	2,800 lb.

On the wire concerned this represents a safety factor of about four. Unfortunately no range of data exists for shroud loadings, and the enormous number of variables in-

volved in the problem and the tremendous labour and expense of collecting and systematis-
ing the data, make it unlikely that the work will ever be undertaken for yachts. It would
probably not be very useful even if completed. A shroud is part of a complicated system
which includes the splices or swages which terminate it, the bolt on which it is hung, the
tang carrying the bolt, the bolt and screws attaching the tang to the mast, and at the other
end the similar members at the chainplate. Empiricism may sometimes be more accurate
than theory.

The first essential feature of a shroud is that the angle which it makes with the mast
should be big enough to give the necessary support. The crucial angle is that between the
shroud and the centreline of the mast, for this governs, for a given loading in the mast
at any point, the amount of tension needed in the shroud to resist it, and the amount of
compression which will be thrown into the mast by the loading in the shroud.* Hence
the use of spreaders, which allow the rigging's angle of spread to be enlarged. As it is
increased, the loadings, tensile and compressive respectively, in the shroud and mast,
are reduced. Shroud angles range between about 12°, which is too small, to about 20°,
which is rarely attained in modern rigging plans.

The difference in mast and shroud loadings when using a narrow or wide spreader
is shown by the conventional methods of graphic statics in *Fig. 24*. The first staying plan
belongs to a narrow boat with a spreader which gives an angle to the masthead shroud
of only 10°. The second is a beamy boat with a wide spreader, producing an angle of
20°. The wider spreader and rigging base results in the following reductions in the
shroud and mast stresses:

(i) Fifty per cent reduction in the compression in the mast below the spreader.
(ii) Forty-five per cent reduction in the compression in the mast above the spreader.
(iii) Fifty per cent reduction in the tension in the lower shroud.
(iv) Forty-five per cent reduction in the tension in the masthead shroud.

The great reduction in rigging stresses produced by a wide spreader will now be
apparent. The most important factor which limits the length of this strut is the need to
sheet overlapping headsails, and with the reduced width of spreader thus imposed an
adequate shroud angle is often attainable only by having more than one set of spreaders.
In inshore racing craft higher stresses in the rigging and mast may be accepted than in
cruisers and offshore craft, in which sufficient width or number of spreaders is a fundamental of safety.

It will be apparent that the strength of the mast as a braced strut depends on the
security of its spreaders. The loss of a spreader may not be fatal to the mast; it was not so
when *Gulvain* lost a lower spreader in the Atlantic in 1950, but when the 40-tonner
Firebird X had one of her swinging spreaders fold up in the Dinard race of the previous
year her mast followed suit. It is at least likely in a seaway that the loss of a spreader will
be followed by that of the mast.

In theory a spreader is a strut in compression, and to assist towards this end it
should bisect the angle of the shroud, where the latter passes over the clevis of the spreader.
This eliminates any bending moment in the vertical plane. But horizontal bending moments can only be avoided if a spreader is free to swing through a small arc forward and

---

* *See page* 84.

aft. Every mast is to some extent a "sinuous horror" when in a seaway, especially when the yacht is pitching. This pulsating of the mast forward and aft throws periodical bending moments into the weather spreaders, and to a reduced extent into the lee ones also. When the mainsail is eased off it bears heavily on the lee spreaders, and this introduces a bending moment from a different cause.

Swinging spreaders have been used for many years, but even inshore they are of doubtful value. Offshore their natural weaknesses are accentuated, and though ocean racers and cruisers have carried swinging spreaders, they have also carried them away. The extent of the swing has to be limited by stops; where these have not been fitted spreaders have overswung and collapsed forward or aft. In a seaway the leeward spreaders, unrestrained by the

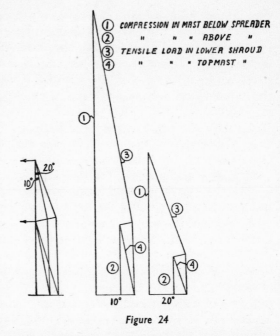

Figure 24

relatively slack rigging, swing to and fro between the stops, producing after a time danger of fatigue failure in the fitting or damage to the stops. Spreaders are therefore generally socketed rigidly, or in a few cases have a slightly flexible bush mounting, as in the Laurent Giles-designed assembly in Plate 9.

At the end of the spreader the shroud passes over the clevis, where it is retained by seizing or by a screw which closes the clevis. The securing of the shroud into the spreader is important, and occasionally overlooked. Sometimes two shrouds, the masthead and intermediate, are both arranged to pass over the clevis of the lower spreader. There is no good reason for this, and the better practice is to adjust the widths of the upper and lower spreaders so that the upper shrouds pass clearly inboard or outboard of the lower spreaders without touching them. Alternately, the requisite small amount of clearance at the spreaders may be obtained by allowing a few more inches separation than usual between the upper and intermediate shrouds at the chainplates. This has the advantage of enabling the spreaders to be the same width, which some may think more seamanlike in appearance.

The position and spacing of the spreaders should apparently be governed primarily by the need to obtain the required angle in the shrouds. In fact, many details of the rig have to be considered in deciding the spreaders' positions on the mast. We need, firstly, one set of spreaders or struts at the point on the mast where the forestay leaves it. From this we develop shroud plan A in *Fig. 25*, which is the simplest, cleanest, and in many ways the most effective arrangement which has been devised for the ubiquitous sloop. It suits small boats, and has been effective in cruisers of from 5–15 tons T.M., and sometimes larger.

In this arrangement the staying of the top of the mast depends on jumper stays passing over jumper struts situated at the forestay attachment. These stays have the twin function of keeping straight, in the athwartship plan, the length of mast above the spreader, and of supporting the top of the mast, above the struts, against the backward pull of the standing backstay. The latter is the less difficult task, and this arrangement makes long jumper struts necessary, angled at 90° or slightly more, and giving an athwartship spread to the jumper stays comparable with the masthead shrouds which they replace.

This layout does suffer from the disadvantage of making it less easy to control the straightness of the top of the mast than with other arrangements shown; for the setting up or slacking of the jumper stays affects both the athwartship and fore and aft bending of the mast, whilst at the same time the tension in the jumper stay needed for athwartship control must be higher than in the case of a shroud.

In the case of a sloop the principal factor governing the position of the spreader below the jumper struts is the need to obtain a big enough angle of spread for the intermediate shrouds—which demands that the spreader should be wide or fairly high—and simultaneously a big enough angle of spread to the lower shrouds—which demands that the spreader should be low. The width of the spreader is limited by the Genoa sheeting; and so, compromising in the various angles, the position of the lower spreaders is settled.

In making the compromise it is generally better to make a sacrifice of angle in the lower than in the intermediate shrouds. The force diagram in *Fig. 24* misleadingly suggests that the load in the lower shrouds is much greater than that in shrouds leading from higher up the mast; but it must be remembered firstly that only one lower shroud is allowed for in this diagram, whereas in fact the load will usually be shared, albeit not quite equally, between two; and secondly, unless the mast is stepped on deck, it gains some of the support of a buried column as a result of being fixed at the step and deck, and hence carries itself some of the load which would otherwise fall in the lower shrouds.*

Shroud arrangement A (*Fig. 25*) may, at the cost of weight and windage, be elaborated to that shown in B, the top of the mast here having, as well as jumper stays, the support of masthead shrouds passing over spreaders at the same level as the jumper struts. Now the purpose of the jumpers is primarily to serve as fore and aft staying. They should be angled farther forward, and their work being less onerous the struts may be shorter than in arrangement A.

Jumper stays fitted thus are better able to restrain the fore and aft bending of the mast than those in A. The tendency of a Bermudian mast, particularly when sailing on the wind, is to bow aft at a little below the middle of its length. This is due partly to the compression put in the mast by the main halyard, and partly to the drag aft of the mainsail transferred through the track. This tendency is resisted by the forward component of the jumper stays' pull at their lower attachment.

In both the above arrangements the mast is split into two panels. When the mast is long in relation to the beam, and hence to the staying base, or when the sheeting of headsails demands very narrow spreaders, three panels may be necessary in order to retain an adequate shroud angle. This leads naturally to arrangement C. Here the work of the jumper stays is not heavy, and their function is divided between holding up the top of the mast athwartships against the small load applied by the drive in the top of the mainsail,

See page 87.

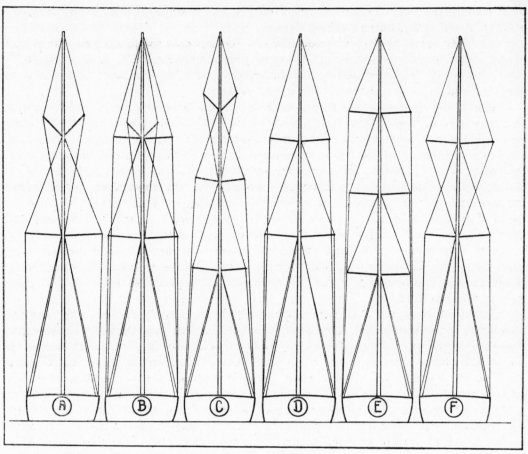

Figure 25.—Shroud arrangements.

and in counterbalancing the pull of the backstay. The jumper stays are, of course, placed at the point of the forestay attachment, and in this arrangement the length of the mast below this point has the support of two spreaders instead of the one of arrangements A and B.

Which arrangement is adopted will depend partly on the size of the boat. The most complex of the three, arrangement C, is found in many modern sloops of only 24 ft. on the waterline, whilst the simpler arrangement A has been successful in cruisers of up to 35 ft. L.W.L. In each case, if a topmast forestay is fitted the jumper struts and stays will be eliminated, and in the cases of A and C be replaced by spreaders.

Minor variations may be played upon the above three arrangements. There is a tendency nowadays, especially when using stiff alloy masts with little taper in their upper part, to leave the top of the mast above the forestay bare of rigging. This produces arrangement A, but with the jumpers eliminated. It results in the standing backstay having no supporting forward pull, and will not serve unless the forestay attachment is at least 80 per cent of the mast height. Then, with a stiff mast, it is satisfactory, for there is no need to put great weight in the standing backstay. An example of this method of staying is found in the large American sloop *Gesture*.

It will be apparent that in arrangement C the fact that the jumper stays terminate at the upper spreader prevents their being of help in resisting the backward bow in the mast which was mentioned above. To make them serve this end the jumpers may be terminated at the lower instead of the upper spreaders.

One of the important arguments in favour of the masthead cutter is the security and simplicity with which the mast may be stayed. The basic layout of shrouds in this case is shown in arrangement D. The upper spreader is placed at the point of the inner forestay's attachment. The lower spreader has to be high enough to clear a staysail sheeted inside the shrouds. The spreader widths then have to be arranged to produce the required shroud angles, which means at least 15° for the intermediate and masthead shrouds, and preferably more. If such angles cannot be obtained without excessive width of spreader a third set must be added, the mast being then split into four separate panels, three of them being below the inner forestay. (Arrangement E.) Masts of 75 ft. in length have been stayed, when the beam of the yacht allows it, with two spreaders only; but at this size three will usually be necessary. The two spreader arrangement of D will also suit masthead sloops, the upper spreader being placed at the level of the lower forestay if one is fitted.

Cutters which do not have the masthead rig are now usually stayed on the arrangement of C, the jib stay coming from the root of the jumper struts, the inner forestay from the upper spreaders. Or again here the top of the mast may be left bare of rigging, the jumper stays being eliminated, and the arrangement of the forestays remaining the same.

The above five shroud arrangements and their modifications will be found to include all the best modern rigging practice in the athwartship staying of the mast. There are however two further modifications which may be adopted with the object of saving weight and windage aloft. The first of these is the return shroud (arrangement F). Here the masthead shroud, instead of being carried down to a chainplate, is brought back to the mast, thereby saving a length of wire aloft at the price of making it impossible to adjust this shroud at the deck. The arrangement F would suit a sloop. It has been used mistakenly in the masthead cutter rig; for the diamond shrouds do not give the necessary support to the masthead.

Linked rigging is a second method of reducing the amount of wire aloft. Considering arrangement D, using linked rigging, the loads in the intermediate and topmast shrouds are carried in a single, larger wire from the lower spreader to the deck. A fitting on the outer end of this spreader carries the rigging screw of the masthead shroud, and sometimes of the intermediate shroud also; alternatively this shroud, which is simply the short length of wire between the root of the upper spreader and the outer end of the lower, has its rigging screw below the upper spreader. A single wire from the fitting at the outer end of the lower spreader to the chainplate then carries the combined loads of masthead and intermediate shrouds to the deck.

Whether or not this method is adopted will depend on the relative importance attached to easy adjustment of the standing rigging, and to the saving of weight and windage. With linked rigging not only are two of the important rigging screws aloft, but the control of the shrouds over the mast's straightness is less certain; so that apart from the inaccessability of rigging screws, the adjustment of the rigging is made more difficult. Linked shrouds are found in a number of ocean racers, and in some yachts which have no particular interest in the last fraction of a knot. In the latter case the complication is hardly justified. In cruisers it is a virtue to be able to adjust all shrouds from the deck. It does seem doubtful whether the advantages of the system outweigh its disadvantages even in the purer bred ocean racer.

With masts which are stepped through the deck lower shrouds are not heavily stressed, and though traditionally two lower shrouds are fitted, led to chainplates forward and aft of the mast respectively, it is now not unusual for one of these to be omitted. When one alone is fitted it should be led to a chainplate forward of the mast, where it helps to control the tendency of the mast to bend aft. An arrangement sometimes adopted to-day is shown in the Clark-designed sloop *Ithuriel* (Plate 11). Here there is an inner forestay, led from the root of the spreaders, on which no sail is set. It may be regarded as the substitute for the two forward, lower shrouds, allowing one wire to be used instead of a couple, and placed more effectively for the control of the mast's backward bend. But it is unable to play any part in the athwartship support of the mast, and offers an obstruction to the headsail when tacking; though this is less of a difficulty than might be expected. It is an admirable system of staying, giving greater control of the mast than is possible with either a single or double lower shrouds.

The practice, however, of relying on one lower shroud per side is not generally approved, and it will be found that a majority of designers still follow the older, orthodox arrangement, and also that most yachtsmen who cruise extensively prefer the added security of two.

· 9 ·

STAYS

Standing Backstays.—Standing backstays have been made possible by the elimination of the gaff and the development of Bermudian mainsails having high aspect ratio and booms short enough to clear a stay from the masthead to the stern. This clearance is important. It is essential to ensure than even when the outer end of the boom lifts, as it will when gybing, or when the sheet is slack, there is no danger of it fouling the standing backstay—an obvious precaution sometimes ignored.*

A parrot beak or masthead chock (Plates 12 and 13) carries the standing backstay clear of the mainsail headboard, and gives a little help also in adding to the clearance at the boom's end. It is not satisfactory to run a standing backstay from a masthead without a chock, for a clumsy length of mast is then necessary above the headboard. Plate 12 shows a chock of good design. This is checked into the mast and secured with the fastenings holding the backstay tang. A less satisfactory arrangement is shown in Plate 13. Here the mast is considerably tapered, running off to a small diameter at its head. There are no tangs, and the forestay and backstay are spliced round the mast, this necessitating a short length of mast above the chock. It is not possible to approve of the method of securing the standing backstay to the chock, the wire simply lying on the top of it, held there by a very light metal strap insecurely fastened. The important stresses in a standing backstay are purely fore and aft, but the unavoidable movement of the mast, and the conditions which exist when reaching, put certain athwartship loads in the standing backstay, which its mast attachment must be capable of carrying.

In boats having transom sterns or short counters, or with old-fashion rigs with long booms, it may be impossible to obtain enough clearance aft for a standing backstay. The latter is the case in the West Solent Restricted class, and many of these boats, converted now for more general cruising, have had the main boom shortened and standing backstays fitted. With modern rigs it is often possible to carry a standing backstay within the limits of a transom stern, but where this is not so a bumpkin may be fitted to carry it. This arrangement is adopted in Mr. Eric Hiscock's ocean cruiser *Wanderer III*. It is not ideal, and the argument for a short counter stern is strengthened in such a case; but with the hull and rig shown it is the only solution. It is used in the Vertue class and many small cruisers.

Standing backstays fall into two categories depending on whether or not sails are set from the masthead—that is, on whether the yacht is masthead rigged. When the highest headstay on which a sail is set is below the masthead the function of a standing backstay is mainly a precautionary one. In collaboration with the jumper stays it keeps the upper part of the mast, above the headsails, straight; and in an emergency it may save

---

I leave the above as written, but quote Mr. Humphrey Barton's note on it when he read it: " I wonder? It is perhaps better that the boom should fetch up on the backstay in an accidental gybe than on the runners? The boom will have gained less momentum; it will be less likely to break in half and split the sail; or to rip the runner sheave off the deck; or to tear the lever from its fastenings; all of which I have seen happen. But I have often had the boom trip up on the backstay, and have lost nothing. Of course one should never gybe with a slack sheet."

the mast should the ship be gybed accidentally before the weather runner has been set up. For these purposes no great initial tension is needed in the backstay. But with the masthead rig the standing backstay is the complement of the topmast forestay, which carries the most important headsails in the ship, and it then has to be set up to a high enough tension to carry the great loads resulting from Yankee jibs and masthead Genoas. It is on the standing backstay that the straightness of the headsail luff depends, and it has to be set up hard enough to ensure this. Many craft then present problems; for when the standing backstay is hardened sufficiently to carry the load of big headsails the mast proves unable to stand the compression. It becomes impossible to maintain a straight luff to the headsail.

Twin standing backstays are now sometimes fitted. These give more security, and at the expense of twice the length of wire, though not twice the weight, as each wire may be smaller. They are also a little more effective, when the yacht is heeled and the mast has sagged slightly to leeward, in supporting the headsail luff. In ketches and yawls the twin standing backstays of the mainmast may be led to the port and starboard quarters clear of the mizzenmast (*Fig. 26*) and this arrangement is superior to that of a single backstay with a whip in its lower part passing on either side of the mizzenmast. Ketches and yawls carrying the masthead rig are therefore best rigged with twin standing backstays, though this does sometimes present a problem in the setting of the mizzen staysail.

Certain ketches carry a stay, which for convenience we may call a triatic,* from the mainmast head to a point below the masthead of the mizzen. This spring stay serves as a backstay for the main, but primarily it is a forestay for the mizzen. It passes over a sheave on the mizzenmast and down to the deck, where it has a normal rigging screw adjustment. An alternative method of adjusting the spring stay may be seen in Plate 14. An adjuster stay is led off the spring stay at about two thirds of its length from the mainmast, taken over a sheave at the mizzenmast head, and led down to a rigging screw near the deck. This layout of rigging enables the spring stay to give support to the mizzenmast at two points; but there is not often any necessity for this.

It is a familiar argument of seamanship whether in ketches the two masts should be stayed together, as in the above examples, or stayed independently of one another. In the former case a very strong combination is produced, but the loss of one mast may easily result in the failure of both, and the whip of the mainmast is at all times transferred to the mizzen. On the whole seamanlike practice suggests independent staying if this can be arranged, and an example is shown in the ketch *Iska* by Laurent Giles and Partners (*Fig. 26*). The mainmast is supported by twin standing backstays to the quarters, as in the ketch in Plate 15, but the forward support of the mizzen is provided by jumper stays or shrouds which pass over struts angled well forward of the mast, and which are set up on chainplates equally far forward.

Runner Backstays.—With the gaff rig two sets of runner backstays were often needed, one from the masthead, or from the truck of the fidded topmast (this being the complement of the topmast forestay and the piece of rigging which carried the load of the jib topsail) and a lower backstay carrying the loads of the forestay and jibstay. When the separation at the mast between the latter two stays was considerable, the single part of the

* *Strictly a stay running between the foremast and mainmast heads of a schooner.*

backstay had a span connecting the single part to the two points on the mast. This arrangement did not allow a satisfactory distribution of the load between the forestay and jibstay, but was used—and often is still to-day—to save the inconvenience of separate sets of runner backstays for staysail and jib.

Runner backstays of the older fashion type consisted of two, three or four parts: (i) the upper span mentioned above; (ii) the backstay; (iii) the backstay runner; (iv) the backstay runner purchase. One leg of the runner whip might be led to a chain-

Figure 26.—Independent staying of the ketch *Iska*.

plate, the purchase being on the other. Sometimes both ends of the runner were arranged as hauling parts, the forward one without the purchase being the quick hauling point. Alternatively the whip forming the runner might be omitted, the purchase providing the only mechanical advantage, and this, instead of being in the air, might be on deck. When the use of winches became common, the fall of the tackle would be led to one suitably placed. There were, in fact, numerous combinations of runner whip, purchase, and winch used in handling the backstays of gaff rigged and early Bermudian craft. Five different combinations are shown in the models of two yachts, a Bermudian schooner of the Twenties and a gaff cutter of earlier date, which are beside me at the moment. Certain of the methods still survive; but mechanical methods of handling running backstays have simplified this piece of rigging. We may also simplify the nomenclature and refer to such backstays as runners.

The primary function of a runner is to support the mast against the pull of the headsails and thereby to ensure the straightness of their luffs. Since most modern yachts carry a standing backstay the security of the mast rarely depends on the runners; and even where there is no standing backstay, a yacht may be tacked to windward without endangering her mast, even though the runners be slack, for the hardened mainsheet under these conditions provides the masts' support from aft. It is when reaching and with the wind aft that the security of the mast depends, in boats without standing backstays, on the runners. But on all points of sailing the tautness of the headsail luffs is regulated by them, and their arrangement and handling has to be governed by this purpose.

The first important feature in their arrangement is their drift—that is, their distance abaft the mast. As the drift is increased the tension put in the forestay by a given tension in the runner is also increased. With more drift, therefore, a given tension in the runner will have a greater effect in keeping the forestay taut, but the combined tensions of runner and forestay will also have a stronger tendency to bend the mast. Though it is an unusual fault, there have been boats with light masts, great drift to the runners, and powerful runner winches, in which it was too easy to harden the runner, and a little strength applied to the winch resulted in a bent mast and a slacker, not tighter, forestay. It is possible, in small racing craft with light masts, for runners to have too much drift when the gear for handling them is efficient.

More usually, the problem is to obtain sufficient tension in the forestay. A given tension in the forestay may be obtained with less tension in the runner, and also less compression in the mast, with a greater angle of drift. More drift thus makes a runner easier to set up efficiently, and on this score is desirable, particularly if the gear for handling the runner is not powerful. As a general rule we may say that the drift of a runner should be the same as that of the forestay which it supports. Sometimes the drift of the runners is greater than that of the corresponding forestay—this is the case in many of Mr. Robert Clark's designs. In many craft it is less, in the interests of easy handling.

This is another feature which has to be considered in placing the runners. They have to be capable of being handled quickly and with certainty. The bigger the drift of the runners the harder the yacht is to handle. When the mainboom is eased, more slack has to be overhauled as the leeward runner is let go and carried forward, and likewise more slack has to be taken in when it is set up. Thus the time for handling this piece of gear is increased, whilst the greater amount of slack is more likely to cause a foul aloft.

In many yachts the leeward runner cuts the belly of the mainsail, even when the boom is hardened in for close-hauled sailing. In others, in which the runner has less drift, it is possible when short-tacking—up a river for example—to have both runners set up hard without their interfering with the setting of the mainsail. When close-hauled in a short, quick sea it may sometimes pay to harden the lee runner and prevent the mast jumping. To sail with weight in the lee runner for long periods is a bad practice; but there are times when it is useful. Excessive drift to the runner is an inconvenience, and it may be desirable to reduce the drift and accept the greater tension which must then be put in the runner, and the greater loading in the mast for an equal tension in the forestay.

It will be apparent that the ideal is to do without runners. This may not be possible; but it is a possibility of which advantage might be taken more often than in fact it is, and it would seem that a consideration of the relative gains and losses involved might lead to the elimination of this item of rigging in many craft or designs.

Fig. 27 (a) shows a typical small sloop. The usual way of eliminating runners is to carry the load of the forestay in the standing backstay, transferring it through twin jumper stays. It will be evident from the angles of the wires concerned that a given loading in the backstay will put a magnified loading in the jumper wires, and an even more magnified compressive loading in the top of the mast. Taking average angles and normal, twin jumper wires, the ratios of loadings in the backstay, mast, and each jumper wire will be about 1 : 3·5 : 1·2; that is, the tensile loading in the backstay will put three-and-a-half times that load as compression in the top of the mast, and about one and one fifth times the load into tension in each jumper wire (*Fig. 27 (b)*).

The weakness of this system will be apparent. Unless the top of the mast is excessively strong (and heavy) it fails to remain straight under the load. It bends, letting the forestay sag, and hardening up on the standing backstay only makes the situation worse. Hence the well-known fact that it is rarely practicable to keep a forestay straight by means of a standing backstay and jumper stays alone.

But the system has been made to work serviceably in small craft. Tom Thornycroft used it in his 5.5-Metre *Ambition*; it is employed in the Aas-designed boats forming what is rather surprisingly known as the International One Design class—craft rather larger and much nicer than Dragons—and many small cruisers of about 5 tons are rigged in this way. It is in the U.S.A. that the system is most commonly adopted. Indeed, of the numerous American One Design classes of keel boats of up to 24 ft. on the waterline, it is probably true to say that more then 80 per cent carry no runners.

It can hardly be doubted that a certain amount of efficiency is lost in boats rigged thus, but with correct design the loss need not be great, and to offset it is the reduced weight and windage, and the quicker, easier handling of the boat which becomes possible.

To make the system effective, the jumper struts must be longer than when runners are fitted, giving a bigger angle of spread to the wires and hence reducing both the tension in them and the compression in the top of the mast. As we are saving two sets of runners, their mast tangs, and their gear on deck, we can afford not to stint the size of the jumper struts. The struts should also be placed at less than their usual ninety degree angle apart, this giving the wires a bigger angle fore and aft and again serving to reduce the loading in the wires and mast. The mast should also not be tapered too heavily towards the truck, and at this point about five-eighths of the maximum diameter is desirable.

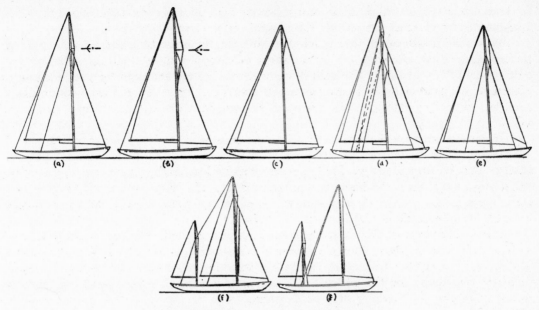

Figure 27.—Runners, back stays and jumper stays.

By these means runners may be eliminated without undue cost in efficiency. But how often do we see small boats rigged as normal sloops which might more easily and effectively be rigged as masthead sloops, when both the runner and the jumper problem are disposed of simultaneously? It is surely hard to understand why the masthead sloop is not more common amongst that numerous and ever-growing fleet of small cruisers ranging between four and seven tons; or in the multitudinous One Design classes of half-decked keel-boats. In the U.S.A. Olin Stephens has rigged several boats of 27 ft. on the waterline, and of heavy displacement too, as masthead sloops.

If we now rig the boat in *Fig. 27 (b)* with a topmast forestay, omitting the lower forestay and jumpers *(Fig. 27 (c))* and put the same load in the standing backstay as before, the compressive loading in the masthead will be only five-eighths of that previously carried. Even if the weight of the backstay be increased to ensure tautness in the rather longer forestay, the masthead will still be less heavily loaded. Surely it is sometimes an un-reasoning conservatism which still clings, in small cruisers, to the sloop rig with a fore-triangle below the masthead?

It is in the cutter that the temptation to eliminate runners is at its strongest. For, unless we are careful, the cutter can become an unhandy ship with two sets of runners, or an inefficient ship with only one set *(Fig. 27 (d))*. Again, the surest way of eliminating runners is to adopt the masthead rig *(Fig. 27 (e))* with twin standing backstays giving excellent security to the masthead and upper forestay, while a single set of runners takes care of the inner forestay carrying the staysail. The growing popularity of this rig is amply justified on theoretical and practical grounds in cutters of the sizes now common. In large cutters, however, the great length of the topmast forestay and the tremendous forces generated by the biggest yankee jib or Genoa make it impossible, even with efficient backstays, to retain a straight mast, and it becomes essential to reduce the size of the fore-triangle. But such craft are outside the normal range of yachts to-day.

When the masthead rig is not adopted, the runners may be arranged with a whip in their upper parts allowing the two forestays to be supported by the single set of runner gear on deck (*Fig. 27 (d)*). The gain in convenience is here attended by a serious loss of efficiency, the total load put in the runner on deck being split between the two forestays, resulting in neither getting enough support to provide a straight luff in any weight of wind.

In cutters with the fore-triangle below the masthead and two independent sets of runners, the forward set may be arranged with only small drift—possibly somewhat less than that of the inner forestay. Then they will require less frequent handling, and may be left set up except when the boom is well squared off. If a cutter has a low forestay and small staysail this layout is easier to arrange efficiently than in boats having a bigger proportion of their total headsail area in the staysail.

It is perhaps more logical to dispense with runners in the ketch than in any other rig, for this rig is usually adopted for the sake of easy handling; it has a fairly short mainmast well suited to carry the masthead rig; and the elimination of gear attached to the mainmast helps to compensate for the added complication of a mizzen. A conventional ketch is shown in *Fig. 27 (f)*, which may be compared with the masthead rig over the same hull and giving the same total sail area in *Fig. 27 (g)*. Here the shorter mainmast is given the greater security of twin standing backstays, runners are eliminated and the triatic also.

A further simplification is achieved by spreading the mizzen shrouds sufficiently to make the runners redundant on this mast. Sometimes, with tall mizzens, a compromise may be effected and a stay fitted with a quick release device requiring operation only when the mizzen is squared off for running. This supplies more support than is provided by a permanent shroud and more convenience than is possible with a runner having greater drift.

Forestays, Jibstays, and Headstays.—In a sloop there may simply be one forestay. Alternatively this stay may be double. There may be a headstay also, and in the mast-head sloop this will carry a sail; otherwise it is a substitute for jumper stays and serves only to keep the top of the mast straight against the tension of the standing backstay. In cutters there will be a forestay and jibstay, and though in older style cutters there may also be a head or maintopmast forestay, carrying a jib topsail, modern cutters either have the jibstay to the masthead, or have jumper stays supporting the top of the mast.

In the sloop rig a single forestay has its dangers. The whole rig is hung on this one wire if, as is now usual, jumper struts and stays are used instead of the older fashion masthead forestay. With reasonably competent maintenance it is unlikely that the wire itself, which will be as strong as any in the ship, will fail. The danger lies in the rigging screws and solid metal terminal fittings at deck and mast. An invisible fault in a tang or deck eyeplate, or fatigue in a once-adequate fitting, can lead to dismasting.

For the purer type of cruiser it does seem that the old style of masthead forestay, even if no sail is set on it, provides a desirable second line of defence ahead of the mast in a sloop. Against it is the interference it causes with the spinnaker, the additional weight and windage of the wire itself, and the tendency of the upper forestay to take some of the load out of the lower where it is needed to keep a straight luff. In deep water cruisers such handicaps may be accepted as the price of safety.

The problem is not perfectly solved in the type of masthead sloop which carries her working headsail on an inner forestay, for when the upper forestay is in use and the lower has been released and carried back to the mast, we are again faced with everything depending on a single forestay. But at least the danger has been reduced, for the upper forestay will be used in relatively light weather only, and in the event of a breakdown the wire luff rope of the Genoa may hold the rig up until the inner forestay is reconnected. The luff rope in a 12-tonner performed this admirable feat once in a fairly steep sea off the Needles. But wires sewn into sails are not inspected often enough to be relied on.

A certain number of modern sloops have appeared with masthead forestays, on which no sail is set, instead of jumpers. Lieut.-Colonel Blewitt's Nicholson-designed *Larph*, of 35 ft. 9 in. on the waterline and carrying 620 sq. ft. of sail area, is one. The Clark-designed cruising ketch *Silver Lining* of 16 tons has a masthead forestay, but the inner forestay, which is close to the outer at the deck, has no release arrangement, and though there is a Genoa to set on the upper forestay, it will probably spend most of its life in its bag, the owner being a confirmed single-hander. Eric Hiscock's new sloop *Wanderer III* also has a masthead forestay on which a Genoa is set; when sailing under lowers the mast is therefore well supported by two wires and their attachments.

There is no doubt that the cutter, even for yachts of below 10 tons, scores points for prudent seagoing with its two relatively lightly loaded forestays, and its mast which is always supported from two points by these stays. The masthead sloop's mast when bereft of support from the inner forestay and carrying sail on the headstay, is being tested pretty highly. The small cutter is a bore when short tacking. But the added security which this rig gives to the mast is strongly in its favour when cruising off-soundings.

Double or twin forestays are in disrepute owing to the tendency of the sail hanks to close round both wires when the sail is flogging. The jam aloft which follows may put the boat out of control until it is cleared, and one boat has, I believe, been wrecked from this cause, the jam occurring when she was beating off a lee shore. Having experienced this trouble once and witnessed it twice, I agree that double forestays are to be avoided except for in-shore racers, where the saving of time in changing headsails is worth the risk of an occasional jam.

If the twin forestays are on levers, however, allowing the idle stay to be slacked off, the danger of a jam is obviated, and there is the further advantage that the idle stay, carrying no tension, does not detract from that in the working one. It is possible that the slacked idle forestay would, if suddenly called on to do its job, keep the mast with the ship, though allowing it to bend alarmingly. Twin forestays on levers at the deck thus give convenience and additional security; those with only ordinary bottlescrew adjustments at the deck are suspect. An arrangement of twin forestays with levers is seen on the foredeck of *Erivale* in Plate 17.

For many years inshore racing craft of all sizes up to J-class boats have used double forestays passing through the deck, over a sheave on the stem, and thence to some type of gear for setting them up below deck. To-day this will usually be in the form of levers, and in small racing craft these are usually arranged one on either side of the heel of the mast.

SHEETS AND HALYARDS

Mainsheets.—To-day the mainsheet is usually the most complicated tackle in a yacht. This is to be expected, for it is used to handle the biggest of the working sails, and often to do so without the help of a winch; though it will be found with many mainsheet purchases that a winch is needed to harden in the last inches when close hauled in any weight of wind.

There are two important requirements for a mainsheet purchase: (i) To have sufficient power to handle the area of canvas with the crew available; (ii) To be suitably arranged for effective handling under all conditions. The first necessitates the tackle having a sufficient number of parts for its purpose. The second depends on the layout of the tackle, particularly on the lead of the hauling part or parts. To some extent the two requirements conflict. If there is enough power to handle the sheet under the worst conditions it will be slow to trim at other times owing to the excess power and consequent length of rope which has to be hauled through the blocks. Hence the value of an arrangement which combines a purchase with a winch for use when necessary.

The simplest of all mainsheet leads is shown in *Fig. 28*, this being suitable for knockabout dinghies and very small boats. The power, it will be seen, is two, there being two parts in the block on the boom. From this block the sheet is rove through quarter blocks to port and starboard. It is thus double-ended and may be trimmed on either side. For small mainsails, up to about 100 sq. ft., this simple tackle fulfills the two requirements for a mainsheet.

For mainsails of between 100 sq. ft. and 250 sq. ft. a power of three in the sheet is convenient, and it may be arranged as in *Fig. 29*. This is a single ended sheet rove through two single blocks and with the fall coming from the block on the boom. Alternatively, the fall may be led along the boom to another block and thence down to a cleat or winch. This carries the hauling part of the sheet forward, clear of the helmsman and to a position where a winch may be fixed or where the crew may work on it conveniently. This lead is found in many small racing craft, such as 5.5-Metres (Plate 18) and though in these craft a winch is usually fitted, the purchase alone gives enough power for one man to handle a mainsail of 200 sq. ft.

It should be noted that a small loss of power results from leading the mainsheet forward along the boom. If we assume that the lead block is placed half way between the gooseneck and the outer block it will be seen that the leverage at B (*Fig. 29*) is only 50 per cent of that at A. When the sheet is led direct from the outer block on the boom the power is three; but when led forward the power is two-and-a-half as a result of the halving of the leverage in one-third of the tackle's parts. On the other hand, the speed of trimming is increased in the proportion that the power is lost.

If this sheet is rove in the opposite way, the standing part being led from a becket on the lower block and the fall leading also from this block, the power is reduced from three to two, there being then only two parts in the block on the boom. This is a lead favoured in racing dinghies, the hauling part being near the helmsman's hand, usually being led along the tiller from the lower block. It has the disadvantage, compared with the double-ended sheet lead with quarter blocks in *Fig. 28*, which gives the same power, of needing a traveller or horse for the lower block; but it is a more convenient purchase for quick handling by the helmsman.

Mainsheet purchases having a power of four are the most common, and are found in craft ranging from half-decked dayboats—X-class boats for example—to 12-tonners and even larger. This power is therefore used to control sails of from 150 sq. ft. to 500 sq. ft. For the former area it is unreasonably high, producing a cumbersome and often friction-ridden tackle which is slow to operate; for the latter it is not powerful enough to harden the sheet in any weight of wind without the help of a winch. A mainsail of 400 sq. ft. cannot usually be trimmed satisfactorily without luffing when using only a four part purchase. Between about 450 sq. ft. to 1,000 sq. ft. a power of five is needed, and with the latter area either a winch or several good hands will be required to harden in the last inches.

There are various ways of reeving the ubiquitous four-part tackle, but though the differences of detail—the exact method of rigging the blocks whether front or side shackle blocks are used, and so on—are numerous, the leads may be classified into a relatively few main types. Initially we may split them into (i) single ended and (ii) double ended purchases, and these may each be subdivided into (*a*) sheets with the hauling part or parts aft, and (*b*) those in which they are led forward.

The advantages of double ended sheets are firstly that they may be handled either to port or to starboard, which is a particular convenience when the falls are aft and probably close to the helmsman; and secondly that the sheet may be overhauled to ease the wear on the rope. Mainsheets led forward have the advantage, which we have seen in the simple arrangement of *Fig. 29*, of being better situated for easy handling; clear of the helmsman and headsail sheet winches, and convenient for its own winch if one is used. It will be evident that the best lead will depend on the layout of the cockpit and the position of the helmsman.

Figs. 30, 31, 32, and *33* show double-ended, four-power, mainsheet purchases having the leads aft. The tackle in *Fig. 30* has two single blocks on the boom, with a single block amidships on deck below the end of the boom, and single quarter blocks to port and starboard through which the two hauling parts are rove. Various modifications of this basic system may be adopted. The middle deck block may be shackled to a horse or a length of deck track allowing athwartship movement, as in *Figs. 31* and *32*, and Plate 19, and a more effective control of the mainsail when the sheet is started.* The blocks may face fore and aft, instead of athwartships as shown. The two blocks on the boom (*Fig. 30* and Plate 19) are placed alongside one another on a single fitting, but an alternative arrangement is to attach them to separate fittings, one forward of the other and from six to nine inches apart. This spreads the load but produces a less fair lead. The same sort of purchase may be used for a single-ended sheet, when one of the quarter-blocks is replaced by a deck eyeplate to which the standing part of the sheet is shackled.

The sheet lead in *Fig. 31* is essentially the same, but the two single blocks on the boom are replaced by one double block. This allows a neater and perhaps stronger fitting on

* *See page* 166.

I

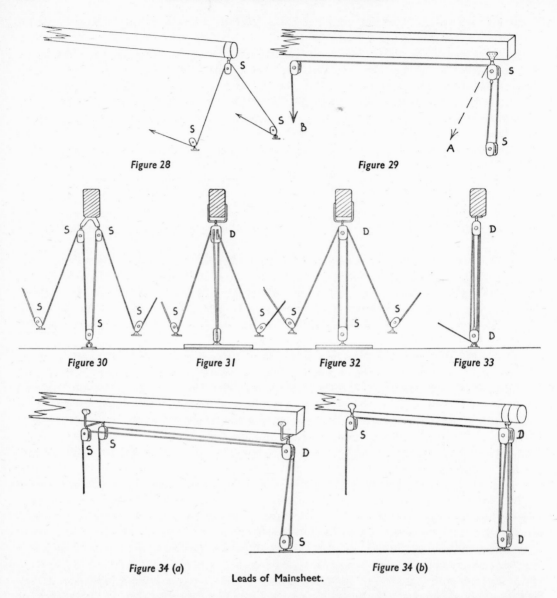

Figure 28   Figure 29

Figure 30   Figure 31   Figure 32   Figure 33

Figure 34 (a)

Leads of Mainsheet.

Figure 34 (b)

the boom, and is generally preferred in bigger craft to-day to the two-block arrangement. The double block and deck block may face athwartships (*Fig. 32*) if this produces a fairer lead, and as before the deck block may ride on a track or horse, or be secured on the centreline to an eyebolt. This same basic arrangement may be adopted using a treble block on the boom and a double block below it on deck; but this gives a power of six, which is higher than will be needed in yachts of to-day's size.

A single-ended mainsheet which is trimmed aft is shown in *Fig. 33*. The fall is belayed on a cleat near the centerline, generally abaft the cockpit coaming. It will sometimes be found that a mainsheet which is secured near the end of the boom produces a difficult lead, the cockpit perhaps extending abaft the boom's end. The sheet may then be fixed to the boom a number of feet forward from the end, the deck block and track being on a bridge deck or horse spanning the cockpit ahead of the helmsman. This layout has two disadvantages: the leverage of the sheet is reduced, as we have seen, and if the boom is light there is the further possibility of its outer end, aft of the sheet attachment, bending and producing a badly setting sail.

Sheets led forward are usually more convenient than those which have to be trimmed aft, and they have the further advantage of distributing the stresses to several points along the boom, reducing the bending moment in the boom and also the load carried in each fitting. An arrangement often adopted with mainsails of from 200 sq. ft. to 500 sq. ft. is shown in *Fig. 34.* Here the deck block is single, on an eyebolt or traveller, the outer boom block is double, and the two falls of the sheet are led forward to two single blocks. Usually a winch is incorporated with this arrangement—with the bigger mainsails it is essential—and one of the falls is taken round the barrel of the winch and the other belayed direct on a cleat, both of which are near the centreline. By this means one part of the sheet is instantly available for quick trimming in light conditions whilst the other, round the winch, will harden in the boom when the purchase's power of four is insufficient. This may be regarded as the modern equivalent of the arrangement used in the old, large yachts when a grab tackle was clapped on to one fall of a double-ended mainsheet for trimming in hard weather.

A further advantage of double-ended sheets may be mentioned here, and that is the possibility which they offer for quick trimming—when gybing round a mark for example—if a man hauls on each fall. Two men will thus overhaul the slack twice as quickly as one. But it is essential that the falls should be in a position where two men can work clear of the helmsman and those tending the headsail sheets; and this almost certainly means that the sheet should be led forward as in *Fig. 34 (a).*

A power of five is needed with big mainsails, and becomes desirable at about 600 sq. ft., or less if quick trimming without a winch is wanted in moderate winds. A single-ended sheet of power five (excluding the loss of power due to reduced leverage in the hauling part) is shown in *Fig. 34 (b).* The first consists of two double blocks, with the standing part of the sheet secured to the becket of the block on the boom, and with the fall of the sheet led forward through a lead block on the boom. The arrangement in Plate 32 has a double block on deck and a triple one at the outer end of the boom, this allowing the sheet to be double ended and the falls to be led forward. The power is six, neglecting losses, or five and a half allowing for the lead forward. This purchase makes an excellent mainsheet for sails of about 900 sq. ft. Such an area may be found in craft of from 35–45 tons T.M., and two or three hands tailing on the mainsheet will be able to trim the mainsail in all but heavy conditions. A power of six will not often be needed in the mainsheets of modern yachts (Plate 21). Such high power makes trimming too slow under normal conditions, and even in the J-class boats, which carried mainsails of up to 4,700 sq. ft., a six-part mainsheet was used, to which a jig was clapped when necessary.

The above review does not exhaust the types of mainsheet tackles which have been used, but it includes most of those which are suitable for modern yachts. The efficiency of any purchase will depend on the arrangement of its details, on the use of twisted shackles and blocks situated so as to avoid chafe in the parts of the rope and in the mortices of the blocks. The design of the fitting carrying the boom blocks must be studied.* Nowadays bails are commonly used (Plate 21). These make a secure attachment, and if designed as in Plate 21, which is superior to the simpler attachment in Plate 32, the shackle of the boom block is allowed to ride well to the side of the boom when the sheet is started, thereby reducing the severe twisting stress which otherwise falls in the non-swivelling gooseneck. Leads for the sheet under the boom are also desirable when the sheet is led forward and ideally these should have wooden rollers which reduce friction to a minimum. It was at one time usual to sling the boom blocks of the mainsheet from a wire strop or sling held on the boom by stirrups, but now the various metal fittings are more usual and are certainly simpler. The strop attachment is shown in Plate 8, the boom block of the purchase riding on a span or saddle shackle. With very large mainsails and heavy booms a sheet buffer, consisting of a rubber block for shock absorption, may be used (Plate 21) but this fitting is now rarely found in craft of below 50 tons.

Headsail Sheets.—Wire has become usual for these in recent years, even in small boats. There are certain good reasons for this. With large headsails having overlap single part wire sheets are essential if the need for a hand forward when tacking is to be avoided. Thus Genoas, Yankee jibs, and other staysails have single part wire sheets with a rope tail worked in with a long taper splice. Also to avoid fouling forward, sheets may be spliced direct into the clew cringle of the sail, and as a further precaution a non-fouling span may be attached between the port and starboard sheets a little way back from the cringle. Wooden rollers on the shrouds help to reduce friction and chafe when trimming big headsails, and in Plate 20 two such rollers will be seen, above the encased rigging screws of the intermediate and upper shrouds. Rope will be used, except for the short, wire pendant at the clew, for double headsail sheets. Nylon rope has not on the whole proved satisfactory. Its stretch, low resistance to chafe, and its slipperiness, which makes it difficult to belay, are against it.

Suggested sizes for wire headsail sheets, based on the area of the sail, are shown in the full line in *Fig. 35*. The rope tails are usually about double the circumference of the wire, though less than this is sometimes chosen. Sheets should be long enough for there to be wire on the drum of the winch when the sail is fully started, and the taper splice ensures a smooth transition on the drum from rope to wire when hardening the sheet after going about.

Splicing sheets into the clew entails a set of sheets for each sail, and also means that the sheet has to be re-rove with each change of headsails. In many boats the headsail sheets are kept permanently on deck, ready rove, when the sheets are shackled in the clew cringle of the appropriate headsail. If an ordinary screw shackle is used in this position the bow type is preferable to the more common D-shape, which is liable to twist in a flogging sail.

When the overlap of a headsail is not great the objection to a two-part sheet is less strong, but they still cause difficulty when tacking, a hand being needed forward to clear the sheet and overhaul the purchase. Plate 22 shows the usual lead for a two-part staysail sheet. The wire pendant from the clew of the sail has a bullseye—a block of hardwood

---

* *For roller reefing booms see page 158.*

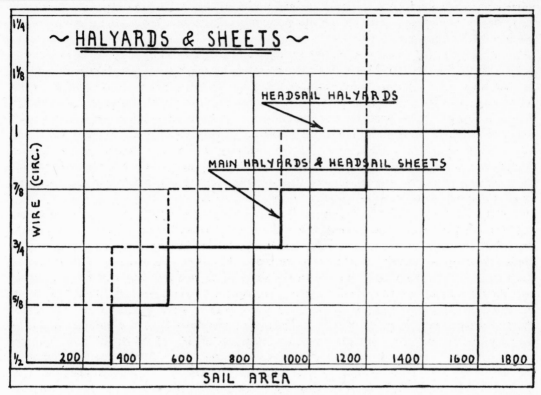

Figure 35.—Sizes for wire headsail sheets.

with a hole in it—stropped into its end. An ordinary single block may be used in this position, and instead of being stropped it may be shackled to the pendant. Through the bullseye or block the two-part hemp sheet is rove, one leg of which goes through the forward bonnet on deck, where it is secured with a stopper knot. The hauling part is led through the after bonnet, and in the boat illustrated goes from there direct to a sheet winch. If there is no winch a purchase may be rigged in this part of the sheet, abaft the second deck bonnet, and a luff tackle or guntackle is usual in this position. The forward block of the tackle is shackled to the end of the sheet a few feet abaft the bonnet, and the after single block is shackled to a deck eyebolt. To obtain a power of three in the gun-tackle the fall is led from the forward block of the purchase. Sometimes the purchase is rigged at the clew of the sail; but this entails blocks and tackles flogging in the air, and it is a less satisfactory arrangement.

The deck bonnets shown in Plate 21 are of an excellent pattern giving an easy lead to the rope. The simplest form of bonnet is a metal eye lined with lignum vitae and bolted to the deck. All such sheet leads suffer from the disadvantage of their non-adjustability. A vital feature of headsail sheeting is the precise angle of the sheet lead,* which ideally must be varied with the point of sailing, the wind strength, and the cut of the

* *See page* 167.

particular headsail which is set; and the lead positions cannot be pre-determined with any accuracy in the design stage. Hence the value of deck tracks allowing the positions of the bonnets to be adjusted.

Various types of track and bonnet are shown in Plates 23 to 26 & 50. That in Plate 23 is for a small boat—a 5.5-Metre in this case—and the track is of T-section with a metal bonnet lined with lignum vitae, suitable for hemp or nylon sheets, and having a screw which engages with holes in the track. The careful fastening of the track will be noticed. The more usual channel-section track is shown in Plate 23 and the method of belaying the wire headsail sheet should also be studied. It consists of a screw-operated clamp aft of the winch. The jaws are closed on the wire by a single movement of the handle. This fitting holds the wire securely whilst obviating the necessity for a rope tail on the sheet, or the poor practice of turning up wire on a cleat, which cripples the wire and produces permanent twists in it which foul in the fairleads.

Plate 24 shows an orthodox single headsail sheet rig, with the sheet led from an adjustable bonnet on a deck track direct to the winch. It will be seen that the deck tracks are set at an angle to the centreline of the boat, and for all jibs other than Genoas this angle allows the necessary adjustment to the lead. As a first approximation, for trimming the sheet when close-hauled, the line of the sheet of an average jib with a fairly highly cut foot should fall on a line which, if extended along the sail to the luff, lies a little above the line of the mitre in the sail cloths. The mitre runs at right angles to the luff, so the sheet therefore leads from the sail at a slightly greater slope than this right angle. The distance of the lead out from the centreline depends on the speed of the boat and her weatherliness. There has grown up a generally accepted idea that if a line is struck from the tack of the jib, or the headsail stay at the deck, at 10–11° to the centreline, the right position for the sheet lead will lie on this line. This is probably as good an approximation as any, but is no more than an approximation. If therefore the mitre line of the jib is extended to the deck this will give the fore and aft position of the sheet lead with a little latitude for adjustment, and the 10° angle will give its distance out from the centreline at this point. This shows the position for the forward end of the deck track. If this is then secured to the deck at an angle of 10° or 11° to the centreline the necessary range of adjustment will be provided. In free winds, when the sheet is started, the bonnet is moved aft and outboard; but only careful experiment on each point of sailing will enable the exact positions to be determined.

The sheeting of Genoa jibs presents a different problem. With their long, low-cut foots the difficulty here is to place the sheet leads far enough outboard; and in most yachts it is, in fact, impossible, and the best that can be done is to give the deck track as near the rail as possible. The Genoa track may be seen in Plate 24 abaft the track for the smaller headsails. The Genoa track may be fastened on top of the rail, as in Plate 26, or even, in some cases, outside the rail on a strake of timber with its upper surface, to which the track is fastened, sloping outboard at an angle of about 60° to the topsides.

The two forward bonnets in Plate 26 are of the orthodox design. Their adjustment is by means of a screw on a knurled nut which engages the holes in the track, which itself is of T-section. Also on the track is an eye slide, similarly adjusted, to take a snatch block of the type shown in *Fig*. 9. The bonnets, blocks, and their attachments transfer heavy stresses to their tracks, and these have to be strongly bolted to the deck and reinforced beneath. When a track is on top of the rail, as in Plate 26, the rail needs local strengthening, which is provided by knees inside the rail and bolted through the shelf. One of these may be seen in the photograph.

To save the trouble of handling separate staysail sheets this sail may be set on a boom, which makes it self-trimming from tack to tack, but reduces its efficiency under all conditions. The boom is also an uncomfortable and sometimes a dangerous companion on the foredeck. But in cutters, which otherwise have two sets of headsail sheets to trim, the staysail boom transforms a yacht which otherwise would be difficult to handle into one with some of the advantages of a sloop. In cutters used primarily for cruising the staysail boom is justifiable. The sheet works on a deck track or horse, and the end of the sheet is led forward along the boom to the tack of the sail, then through a lead block on deck and aft along the port or starboard side as desired (Plate 27.) A type of staysail boom gooseneck is shown in Plate 28.

Halyards.—Except in the smallest craft halyards to-day are also usually of wire with hemp tails. Wire gives reduced windage, is less likely to part through chafe, and such halyards, unlike those of rope, do not need constantly setting up owing to stretch. A disadvantage of wire halyards is that if they do carry away they are more likely to cause a foul aloft than hemp. In small craft the thin wire is difficult to handle and kinks easily, and in knockabout boats, half-deckers, and those with an orthodox gunter lug rig, hemp is still generally the most serviceable material for this piece of rigging.

Suggested sizes for wire are shown in *Fig. 35*. The simplest rig of main halyard consists of a single wire or rope led over the masthead sheave and down to the deck. This serves for mainsails of up to about 150–200 sq. ft. in area, the final setting up of the sail being achieved by swigging on the halyard. For larger areas a purchase, a winch, or a combination of the two, must be introduced. A single part halyard with a winch is competent to deal with mainsails of up to about 350 sq. ft.

For larger mainsails a two-part purchase may be incorporated in the halyard. A single block is shackled to the halyard so that it is near the masthead when the sail is lowered. A wire whip with a rope tail is rove through this. A power of two is thus obtained, which is enough for the initial hoisting. If a winch is fitted the standing part of the wire whip is secured to an eyebolt at the deck, and the final setting up of the halyard is done by taking a few turns of the rope tail on the winch. The length of the tail should be such that wire is running on the winch during the last few feet of hoisting. If there is no winch a further tackle is rigged in the standing part of the wire whip, which, instead of being terminated at a deck eyebolt, has a single or double block shackled to its end, at about the height of the boom. The purchase is rove between this block and a second secured to the deck. The initial hoisting is done, as before, on the rope tail of the whip, which is then belayed, the final setting up being achieved with the help of the purchase.

For large mainsails, of about 700 sq. ft. and more, double ended main halyards are needed. These entail two sheaves side by side at the masthead, either in a wide mortice in the mast, or, if the mast is excessively tapered, fitted in the form of external cheek sheaves. The shackle for the mainsail headboard is carried on a single metal block lying athwartships, which is best designed for the purpose with a large sheave, flat shell, and fairlead guards for the wire. The halyard is rove through this block, the two ends being then led over the port and starboard sheaves in the mast and down to the deck. If a powerful halyard winch is fitted one of the falls is led to this, whilst the other is secured at the deck. It will be found that in yachts carrying mainsails of up to 900 sq. ft. three men on a single end of such a halyard will be able to get the mainsail half way up or more before finding it necessary to take turns on the winch. If there are no winches fitted a purchase, or two purchases as in the single part halyard, have to be rigged in one end of the double halyard. Apart from the power gained from the block at the headboard a further advantage of the double ended halyard is that the nips of the wire at the mast sheaves need not always fall in the same part of the wire.

Another main halyard lead, suitable for smaller sails, is similar to the above in having a two-part halyard with a block at the mainsail headboard, but one part of the halyard from this block is secured at the masthead a few inches above the sheave in the mast; the other end is led over the sheave and down to the deck and to the usual purchase or winch. A point may here be noted about masthead sheaves; they should always be of slightly larger diameter than the fore and aft dimension of the mast at the mortice, the sheave thus standing out of the mast (Plate 16) and giving a fair lead to the halyard on either side.

When mast winches are fitted headsail halyards may be single for sails of 250 sq. ft. or more, the halyard passing over the mast sheave or block, with the fall led direct to the winch. The alternative to a winch is a tackle which may be hooked to the halyard for the last part of the haul. The fall of the wire halyard has an eyesplice which comes just short of the halyard's mast sheave when the sail is lowered. The rope tail is spliced into this. The sail is hoisted until the wire eyesplice comes within reach. This is then put over the hook on the upper block of the tackle, and the halyard set up with the aid of the purchase.

A purchase may alternatively be rigged at the other end of the halyard. The shackle for the head of the sail is then carried in a single block. The halyard is spliced to the becket of the mast block, rove through this single block, and then back through the mast block and down to the deck. The arrangement gives a power of three, and when this is enough the rig is perhaps more convenient than a separate tackle at the foot of the mast. For large headsails, of 500 sq. ft. and more, this sort of purchase may be used in collaboration with a halyard winch.

Internal halyards are now sometimes used. Their advantage is a saving in windage, and their chief popularity is in the small racing classes (Plate 29). Here the halyards are led out of the mast over sheaves at the heel. The main halyard is set up on the winch. The jib halyard has an eyesplice at the end of the wire, which is passed over one of the hooks on the hookplate, the sail being set up with a tack tackle. In the photograph the rope tails of the wire halyards are shown.

A further method of setting up headsail halyards is the tack tackle mentioned above. In elaborately-rigged yachts the tack tackle may be replaced by a tack winch, four of which may be seen in Plate 17. With this arrangement the halyard is belayed at the mast and the final setting up is done forward with the aid of the tack winch or tackle. Though nowadays common this seems to offer few advantages, while the use of tack tackles or winches in combination with halyard winches on the mast seems wholly unjustifiable, though sometimes seen.

Boom Guys and Kicking Straps.—A boom guy does much to obviate the more glaring weaknesses of the fore and aft rig in following winds. The guy is secured in the vicinity of the boom's outboard end, and is led forward outside the rigging to the stemhead. The objects of the guy are to steady the boom in light winds and a broken sea, when without one the sail will slat against the slack mainsheet and spill the wind; and in heavier weather to prevent an accidental gybe. With a guy rigged a better course will be steered in strong quartering and following winds, when anxiety to avoid a gybe as the boat yaws will otherwise result in the helmsman steering perhaps points high on the proper course.

To reduce the load in the guy it should be secured as near the outboard end of the boom as possible, and also as far forward on the stemhead as can be arranged. In its simplest form a guy is simply a single part of rope led through a block rigged near the stem, and with the fall belayed on the foredeck. To enable the guy to be set up hard against the pull of the mainsheet, and thus hold the boom rigid, a purchase is generally needed in the inboard end of the guy, and it is always convenient to lead the fall of the guy purchase aft to the cockpit. Then the mainsheet and guy can be trimmed together from aft, and it is not necessary for a man to go forward, where he is out of touch with those trimming the mainsheet.

Elaborate guys embodying shock cord have been used, but the elastic shock absorption hardly seems necessary. Single part wire guys, with a snap shackle at either end, led from the stem through snatch blocks near the weather rail to a winch aft, are also used. These are reversible, which simplifies the operation of re-rigging the guy when gybing, the former outboard end of the guy, before gybing, being led through the snatch blocks on the new weather side, and the former hauling end being tacked off the winch and secured to the boom.

The purpose of a kicking strap is to replace the strong downward component of the mainsheet's pull, which is diminished as the sheet is started, allowing the boom to lift and throw twist into the mainsail.

This twist is definitely harmful. It is true that in theory the wind is freer aloft than at the deck level, since a velocity gradient of wind over water shows about 30 per cent increase in wind speed at 20 ft. above the surface compared with that at 5 ft. But for various aerodynamic reasons, one of which concerns the effect of the hull itself upon the air flow around it, the velocity gradient is profoundly modified, and in practice the difference in wind speed at the boom's level and near the top of the mainsail is probably negligible. If a mainsail is twisted it means that at only one level is the sail trimmed at its optimum angle to the wind; at other levels the angle of incidence is either too great or too small.

The kicking strap usually takes the form of a purchase secured at about the mid-length of the boom, and led either to the foot of the mast or to the lee rail. With the former the strap need not be re-rigged when gybing. A kicking strap is obviously most effective (for its primary function of providing a downward pull on the boom) when the deck attachment lies in the same plane as the boom. When secured near the rail a different position is needed for each angle of trim if this is to be achieved.

II

TOPPING LIFTS AND CLEW OUTHAULS

Topping Lifts.—These two pieces of gear, though without any close functional relationship, are conveniently considered together.

The primary functions of a topping lift are to lift or control the boom when hoisting and lowering the sail, and when reefing; a secondary one is to regulate the draft of the sail in light winds by relieving the sail of a part of the boom's weight.

When hoisting a sail the weight of the boom, in all but the smallest craft, should be carried by the topping lift until the sail is fully hoisted. The practice of leaving the boom in its crutch whilst hoisting, until the sail itself lifts the boom as it nears the fully hoisted position, is not a good one. It may produce in time a badly stretched sail resulting from the concurrent loads of the halyard's pull and the boom's weight spreading unevenly over the canvas and producing a hard line in the sail.

With the gaff rig topping lifts in seagoing craft are generally double, led to port and starboard from the upper cup in the case of boats having fidded topmasts, or from the hounds when a pole mast is fitted. The weight of the boom is carried in the weather lift when hoisting and lowering, and it has to be accepted as part of the difficulty of hoisting that the gaff has to be kept clear of the lifts on its way up and down. Double lifts have the further disadvantage of producing chafe, the slackened weather lift riding across the seams of the mainsail when under way; for this reason they may be served with baggy wrinkle. Even with the gaff rig, however, double topping lifts are not invariable. *Dyarchy* is an example of a yacht with gaff rig and a single lift.

The disadvantages of double topping lifts may be obviated with the Bermudian rig, in which the absence of a gaff allows a single lift to be led to the masthead. Yet even to-day Bermudian boats are seen with topping lifts led from low down on the mast in the region of the forestay attachment, owners sometimes even asking for this layout in new craft. It is difficult to see why. It is not seamanlike, except in small vessels, to rely on a single lift rigged thus, for then the sail can be hoisted only to leeward of it; yet two present the extra rope aloft, a greater amount of gear to handle, and the dangers of fouling when hoisting and lowering the sail.

The older, orthodox arrangement with the Bermudian rig is simply to run the lift from the boom's outboard end (where it is shackled on to a band, or to a swivel if roller reefing is used) over a masthead sheave and down to the deck (*Fig. 36 (a)*). When the weight of the boom makes it necessary a purchase is introduced on the hauling part at the foot of the mast. A later arrangement, developed, I think, through ocean racing, is to eliminate the masthead sheave and to shackle the lift here, run it to a sheave at the boom end and then along the boom, where it is belayed at somewhere about mid-length (*Fig. 36 (b)*). This arrangement may also be seen in Plate 8 with the topping lift purchase under the boom, or in bigger boats the lift may run inside a hollow boom on to a winch, also inside the boom.

If a purchase on the boom is fitted, the topping lift may pass over a sheave at the extreme end of the boom, and thenceforward under the boom to the moving block of the tackle. The fixed block is fastened to the boom farther forward, and the moving one slides on a length of track which keeps it close to the boom and free of fouling or slatting, as in Plate 8. The purchase is rove between them, the fall being belayed on a cleat also on the underside of the boom. Alternatively, the purchase may be arranged on the side of the boom, the sheave in the boom being offset (probably having the sheave of the mainsail outhaul offset on the opposite side). If however the gooseneck is of the swivelling type this will make the boom cant when weight comes in the topping lift, and to avoid it with a side sheave the topping lift has to be terminated in a single block a few feet above the boom's end. A wire is rove through this block one end of which is shackled to the top of the boom on the opposite side to the sheave, whilst the other passes round the sheave and thence to the sliding block of the purchase on the side of the boom. Another method, and one in which a side purchase may be combined with the advantage of a centreline sheave, was adopted in the *Myth of Malham*, the lift passing over the centreline sheave, and then through a long hole in the side of the boom, and out to the purchase.

On the score of simplicity it is probably best to have the purchase on the bottom of the boom, where it is easily accommodated on modern rectangular spars. When a topping lift winch is fitted the lift runs inside the boom to the drum of the winch, and this is operated by handles inserted at the side of the boom.

The older method of rigging a topping lift, with the fall at the foot of the mast, has the advantage of providing an extra sheave at the masthead and the topping lift in an emergency may be used as a halyard. Also, when the fall is belayed at the foot of the mast it is perhaps more conveniently placed than on the boom, being near the halyards and in a part of the ship where it is easy to stand and work. The second method saves the weight and windage of the length of wire and rope running down the mast. But it cannot be used with roller reefing.

With the first method it is becoming a common but rather risky practice now to unshackle the lift from the boom end when under way for long periods and to carry it forward to the rigging, this saving the constant chafing of the lift against the seams of the mainsail. Though I have not seen it done, there seems no reason why the same practice should not be adopted with the second arrangement by introducing a shackle at a point which is a little above the sheave in the boom when the lift is holding the boom.

Various other methods or modifications of the above have been tried from time to time. In the Giles-designed *Beyond*, in which the Worths cruised round the world, the lift is of nylon rope shackled to the boom and run over a masthead sheave and led down the mast—the older orthodox arrangement. But the lift, being of nylon, has considerable stretch. This gives sufficient spring for the lift to carry the weight of the boom, or for the boom, when stowed, to be hauled down on to the gallows by the mainsheet, without any hardening or slacking of the lift, which can thus remain permanently belayed. By saving one operation on deck this arrangement has obvious advantages.

Double-ended topping lifts, capable of being adjusted both at the mast and near the end of the boom, have had their advocates, but are not often seen nowadays. When the ordinary single-ended topping lift has its adjustment on the side or bottom of the boom, as described above, the fall has to be belayed far enough inboard always to be accessible. With a double-ended lift the fall on the boom may be near its outer end. This has the advantage of allowing one man to stow the boom, since he can simultaneously lower the boom and guide it into the crutch or gallows.

I have sailed with a topping lift which in theory seems bad and in practice works excellently. It is a lift of fixed length shackled at the masthead, and with a lanyard at the boom end adjusted to give the requisite amount of slack when the mainsail is hoisted, and to hold the boom horizontal when the main is lowered (*Fig. 36 (c)*). The topping lift is simply there and forgotten until needed; and no setting up is necessary. But with such an arrangement it is essential that the angle of the boom when reefed should not differ materially from that under full sail. Also, this arrangement would not be suitable with a big boom owing to the difficulty of lifting the boom into its crutch by hand. It also, of course, makes impossible that refinement of sailing in light winds when some of the weight of the boom may be taken by the topping lift to add flow to the mainsail. · But whether this ever pays is very doubtful.

For many years small class racers, such as 6-Metres and Dragons, have used a very simple form of topping lift which is nothing more than a pendant fixed to the standing backstay a few feet above the boom end. When not in use it is hitched to the backstay; when needed it is shackled to the boom end, a simple clip being used such as a dog-lead spring clip. An elaboration of this method has lately been applied to seagoing boats. The lift is then rove through a fairlead on the backstay, and down to a deck fairlead near which the fall is belayed. The result is a topping lift with less wire in it than in any other,

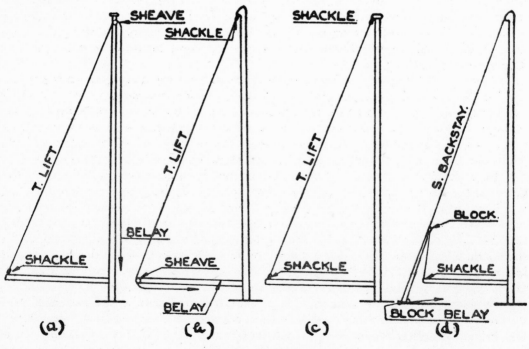

Figure 36.—Topping Lifts.

but one of which there is little experience in seagoing craft (*Fig. 36 (d)*). Inshore the only use of the lift is to keep the boom out of the helmsman's way when the mainsail is lowered coming up to the mooring. There is no question of reefing under way. Off-shore one may wonder about the stresses which the rig may place on the backstay. To avoid these becoming excessive, the lead of the lift from the boom end should be as nearly in the line of the backstay as possible. Stresses in the backstay will be greatest when the lift is led at a right angle from the backstay, for any loading in the topping lift will be greatly magnified in the backstay. In practice the best compromise angle will be where the lift is carried up to the backstay vertically. At least, the lead on the backstay should be as high as possible.

Topping lifts may be of wire or rope. When double lifts led from near the hounds are used rope has the merit of reducing chafe. To-day nylon, with its great strength, is the best material, and as we have seen this may even be used also for lifts coming from the masthead; though then chafe is not a consideration. But wire is now usually fitted, and sometimes the wire chosen is much too light. When reefing, the lift has to support the boom under conditions of high stress, and the safety of the men working at the boom may also depend on it. Lifts rigged so that they may serve as halyards must be strong enough for this work, and part of their advantage is lost if they are not strong enough also to carry a man aloft in a bosun's chair.

This is perhaps a convenient place to say that no piece of rigging which is unnecessary is good. Many small boats of the half-deck type have elaborate topping lifts rigged in spite of the fact that the boom may be lifted with one hand. Either one of the above simplified lifts should be adopted, or none at all; though topping lifts are needed sometimes in tiny boats to keep the boom clear for rowing, picnicking and the like.

A topping lift is needed to support the after end of a staysail boom, when one is fitted. It carries no great weight, but is needed to prevent the boom stretching the foot of the sail. A light wire led from the mainmast at the lower spreader and snapped into an eyebolt at the end of the boom makes a suitable lift for this purpose.

Clew Outhauls.—In general an outhaul is a line used to haul anything, especially a sail, out to a certain position. The clew outhaul of the mainsail is the largest and most important outhaul on board, if we exclude that of the jib traveller in boats with bowsprits. It serves two distinct purposes, only one of which is clear from its name. Firstly it stretches the foot of the sail along the boom and retains in it the necessary amount of tautness. Secondly it holds the clew of the sail down to the boom and resists the very strong upward pull which exists at this point when sailing.

In the simplest form of outhaul these functions may be performed by two lengths of line spliced into the clew cringle of the mainsail. One of these is passed several times to and fro between the clew cringle and an eye on top of the boom at its outer end, the foot of the sail being thus hauled taut. In the illustration of the mainsheet arrangement in Plate 30 a clew outhaul of this elementary sort may be seen on the main-boom. When the sail has been drawn sufficiently taut the line is hitched round itself and secured.

This lanyard alone, however, does nothing to hold the clew of the sail to the boom, which is the function of a second line passed several times through the clew cringle and round the boom. Sometimes one length of line is made to serve the two purposes; but this is not a good practice, and the second line should be rove independently of the outhaul itself.

This arrangement, which is found in many small and simply rigged boats, and occasionally, as in Plate 30, in larger craft also—it is inevitable if roller reefing is fitted—has many faults. It is clumsy and slow to operate, and as a result the adjustments which should be made in the outhaul may be neglected. Yet perhaps we need not worry too much about the latter. In boats in which a lashing outhaul is used, the outhaul is set up in the spring and left sometimes untouched until the autumn, and the mainsail remains undamaged. This is probably due to the stretch in the lanyard, which is able to ease the foot of the sail when required without special adjustment.

A well-rigged outhaul consists of a slide to which the clew cringle is connected; a length of track on which the slide runs; a wire pennant on the slide led over a block at the end of the boom, and forward again to a purchase which is readily accessible. The latter point is important.

Types of slides are shown in Plates 31 and 32. The sail may be attached to the slide directly, being inserted between the ears of the slide and retained there by a bolt passing through the ears and the cringle in the clew of the sail. Alternatively, the connection may be made by means of a twisted shackle (Plate 32). Two refinements may be made in the design of the slide. The upper part of the slide, with the ears and bolt attachment, may be arranged to swivel, this preventing the clew of the sail from being restrained, and allowing the slide to lie in the same plane as the sail and thus relieve itself of any bending moment. This is shown, on an outhaul of a different type, in *Fig. 38*. Secondly, the ears of the slide may have several alternative holes for the bolt, the one used being that which keeps the foot of the sail, between the ordinary slides and the clew slide, in a straight line. Without this refinement the foot of the sail at its extreme end may be dragged a little out of shape, and the set of the sail be slightly impaired.

Either at the forward or after end of the slide is a sheave, or if not a sheave a suitably formed groove (Plate 31). Over this runs the wire pennant, one end of which is made fast at the outer end of the boom, whilst the other is led over a cheek block and thenceforward to the rope purchase. It should be noted that with the pendant rove thus a power of two is obtained without allowing for the rope purchase, which will increase it further. An outhaul pennant arranged in this way is shown in Plate 32, the standing end of the wire being shackled to an eyebolt on the boom's starboard side, and the purchase being arranged on the port side. Instead of a two-part pennant and cheek block, the pennant may be single and led direct over a sheave inside the boom, as we have seen may be done for topping lifts; but it is often a desirable simplification to avoid having two sheaves close together in the boom.

The track on which the slide moves has to carry the load of the upward pull at the mainsail's clew. A few feet of heavier and stronger track than that on which the ordinary sail slides run is generally fitted at the end of the boom (Plate 33), this carrying the clew outhaul slide and being bolted through the boom throughout its length. It is easy to under-estimate the strength of the pull upwards which, when under sail in any weight of wind, is continuously trying to drag this track from the boom. Once, when cruising in a fairly large yacht, we bent a mainsail which was a few feet shorter on the foot than the one normally carried, and the clew of which did not reach the outhaul track. Consequently the upward pull at the clew cringle was borne by the ordinary track, and mistakenly no lashing was immediately passed round the boom at this point. A few hours in a strong wind was enough to lift several feet of this track, a number of the screw fastenings drawing suddenly. The careful through-bolting of the outhaul track is thus an important feature; screws which are enough to hold the ordinary boom track are not sufficient here. It has been found, however, that with good, modern track, the size which serves for the rest of the foot of the mainsail will do also for the

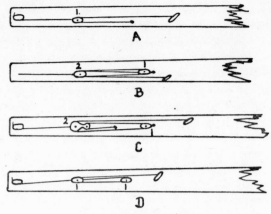

Figure 37.—Main clew outhauls.

outhaul—provided the through bolting is strong enough—and there are designers who now omit the heavier track.

The outhaul purchase may be arranged in various ways (*Fig. 37*) to give the power required, and the arrangements shown are equally suitable for topping lifts. As a guide to the requisite power we may suggest that for mainsails of 100 sq. ft. or less no purchase is needed; between 100–300 sq. ft. a power of two is sufficient (*Fig. 37 (a)*); between 300–700 sq. ft. a power of three will serve (D) and above this a power of four (B and C). Arrangement B is a double and a single block, whilst in C the double block is replaced by a fiddle block, which is flatter and neater for this purpose, and likely to produce a fairer lead. It is best in all cases if the after of the two blocks in the purchases runs on a length of track. Blocks of this type, with a slide mounted on one cheek, are made for the purpose.

The following sizes are suitable for the wire pennants and the rope in the purchases:

Sail Area	Wire Pendant (Circ.)	Rope Purchase (Circ.)
100	$\frac{3}{8}$ in.	1 in.
200	$\frac{3}{8}$ in.	1 in.
400	$\frac{1}{2}$ in.	1 in.
600	$\frac{1}{2}$ in.	$1\frac{1}{4}$ in.
800	$\frac{5}{8}$ in.	$1\frac{1}{4}$ in.
1,200	$\frac{3}{4}$ in.	$1\frac{1}{2}$ in.

Instead of pendants and purchases a mechanical arrangement may be used in the outhaul. One type, which has many variations in detail, is shown in *Fig. 38*. It consists of a threaded rod turned by a hinged handle at the end of the boom which, when not in use, folds downwards into the boom. The rod actuates the clew slide, but the upward strain in the sail is carried by the heavy track in which the slide operates. Arrangements such as this are suitable if roller reefing is fitted, when the various protuberances on the boom of blocks and tackles are not acceptable, and the other alternative is the simple and not always very efficient lashing type of outhaul.

When staysails are set on a full length boom pivoted on the stay at the tack of the sail, an outhaul of the slide and purchase type is needed as on the mainsail. No great power is needed in the purchase, but it must be conveniently arranged, for here the outhaul, unlike that of the main, has to be slacked each time the sail is lowered; otherwise the sail will be badly stretched. This precludes the use of the simple lashing outhaul, which takes far too long to handle. Or, if one is used, it may be left untouched and instead the three or four lowest hanks of the luff be let go before lowering the sail. This procedure will prevent the sail from being girt across; though it may not be so convenient as letting go a neatly rigged outhaul.

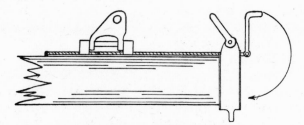

Figure 38.—Screw operated clew outhaul.

12

TANGS AND CHAINPLATES

Tangs.—The traditional method of attaching the shrouds to the mast is by means of eyesplices encircling the mast (Plate 16) and resting on chocks of hardwood—bolsters—fastened to the mast (Plate 34). Throughout the days of sail this was the system used in vessels large and small, and it is still retained in many yachts both gaff rigged and Bermudian. In the best practice the eyesplices in the wire are not only served, but have the serving covered with rawhide to protect the mast.

Again traditionally, the four lower shrouds were attached to the mast in the following order, working from the top eyesplice down to the hardwood bolster:

(i) Port aft shroud.
(ii) Starboard aft shroud.
(iii) Port forward shroud.
(iv) Starboard forward shroud.
(v) Hardwood bolster.

The bunch of eyesplices resting on the bolster constituted the hounds, a term which to-day, with long single-piece masts whose lower shrouds form only one, and a relatively unimportant, part of the lateral staying, has lost its significance.

There are strong objections to this system of attaching rigging, though many of them did not apply in earlier days of sail. The splices tend to " settle " on the mast, with a result that the shrouds lengthen—a disadvantage accentuated to-day when the rigging is set up so hard. The splices are also liable to crush the mast, especially the outer fibres of spruce masts. Masts rigged thus are difficult to unrig. The eyesplices do not sit easily on angular and oval masts. And finally, the encircling eyesplices present peculiar difficulties when on a mast carrying the track of a Bermudian mainsail. The track has to be raised on a hardwood batten, which is then cut in the way of the shrouds, allowing the eyesplices to pass beneath the track.

These objections led to the development of tangs, which may be regarded as chainplates on the mast, with the important correlative implication that the one fitting should be as strong as the other. For many years tangs lay under a shadow as a result of their frequent failure under stress.

Tangs have evolved from the earlier type of mastband or collar, which is still commonly seen. Though such fittings do not entirely obviate the problem of the track, which has to be passed over the top of the band, they are a reasonable solution to the tang problem on round masts (Plates 35 and 36) and their lack of popularity to-day is due to the use of oval and box masts to which bands are not easily fitted. A mast band consists of a circular steel plate to which are welded or riveted angle bars forming lugs for the bolts which clamp the band to the mast. Holes may be cut in the band both to save weight and to allow a firmer grip of the mast, and on to the band are welded the necessary rigging attachments. These consist of eyes to carry runners and halyards, cups or flanged plates for the spreaders, and lugs for the shrouds, while the clamping bolts of the band may

K   141

carry lugs for the forestay and jibstay. A bolt passing through the mast from side to side, and usually also through the lugs carrying the shrouds, anchors the band securely to the mast and prevents twisting. Bands vary in details of their design, and some consist of two separate semi-circular plates bolted to the mast through lugs at the sides, these bolts carrying the thimbles of the shrouds.

A simple tang assembly is shown in Plate 37. It consists of an horizontal band running a little more than half round the mast and passing over three vertical straps, on the port, starboard, and fore sides, each of which is screwed to the mast. On top of the band are three lugs, bolted through the band and lower straps and forming jaw fittings carrying bolts for the shrouds and forestay. An extension of the strap on the fore side of the mast provides the attachment, below the forestay jaw, for the headsail halyard block. The spreader sockets are placed above the jaw fittings and cover the bolt which passes through the mast.

Plate 39 shows a forked tang assembly designed by Mr. Robert Clark for a 40-tonner. This is a more elaborate example of the laminated construction used in the tang in Plate 38. The three straps, arranged in the form of a three-prong fork, lap one another in the lower part of the tang, and there is a fourth lamination of plate over the bottom of the fitting, with a result that both the top and bottom of the jaw carrying the bolt for the shroud consist of a double thickness of metal.

At the other end of the scale of size is the tang assembly designed by Messrs. Laurent Giles for a 6-Metre, and made of aluminium alloy (Plates 10 and 40). The intermediate shroud tang (Plate 10) consists of a single light alloy lug hung on a hollow bolt through the mast, to which is also screwed the tubular spreader, whilst a second bolt gives the fitting rigidity. The tang for the lower shrouds (Plate 40) consists of a similar but larger lug shaped to carry two shrouds, and hung from the same bolt as the forestay fittings.

It will be seen that tang assemblies consist basically of strap and plate fittings screwed to the mast and hung on a through bolt or bolts. The straps are worked into the required shape for the shroud attachments, and other necessary fittings are welded to them. In engineering details tang design to-day shows great variety, and fittings appear sometimes to have a redundancy of metal in them; the result, probably, of a wish to err on the side of security. In Britain tangs are generally made of galvanised steel, and in the U.S.A. manganese and other bronze alloys are frequently used. We may expect aluminium alloy to become common for the mast fittings of small craft.

The following table is a guide to the sizes of the shroud and stay jaw pins and mast bolts of tangs:

Circum. of Shroud	Dia. of Jaw Pin	Dia. of Mast Bolt
$\frac{3}{8}$ in.	$\frac{1}{4}$ in.	$\frac{1}{4}$ in.
$\frac{1}{2}$ in.	$\frac{5}{16}$ in.	$\frac{5}{16}$ in.
$\frac{5}{8}$ in.	$\frac{3}{8}$ in.	$\frac{3}{8}$ in.
$\frac{3}{4}$ in.	$\frac{7}{16}$ in.	$\frac{7}{16}$ in.
$\frac{7}{8}$ in.	$\frac{1}{2}$ in.	$\frac{1}{2}$ in.
1 in.	$\frac{5}{8}$ in.	$\frac{5}{8}$ in.

It is at least arguable that when tangs have long straps carrying numerous wood screws the through bolts are unnecessary; though few tangs have been designed without them. We have before us drawings of a cutter whose intermediate shrouds have a breaking strain of 5 tons. Each tang is secured to the mast with forty $1\frac{3}{4}$ in. wood screws of $\frac{1}{4}$ in. diameter. In a mast of Oregon pine the permissible working load with the arrangement of screws shown would be about $4\frac{1}{2}$ tons, and in a spruce mast about $2\frac{3}{4}$ tons. A tubular through bolt is also fitted; but it will be apparent that a tang redesigned to carry more screws, or a mast with its walls locally thickened to allow a larger diameter of screw, would make the bolt redundant. Tangs fastened by screws alone have been tried successfully in the U.S.A. Great care has to be taken, of course, in spreading the screws over the grain of the mast, and in avoiding lines of screws which follow lines of grain.

Interesting experiments in tang design have been made by one owner who has available elaborate workshop equipment. He made tangs for his 11-ton cutter from $\frac{1}{8}$ in. thick stainless steel plate, which was cut to shape and then had the necessary bosses and fittings welded in position. The tang was then bonded to $\frac{1}{16}$ in. thick spruce with Redux. This is the glue made by Aero Research, which was used, instead of riveting, for fastening together the Comet airliner. After bonding the tang was put through rolls to bend it to the shape of the mast, and the bond remained intact under this severe test. The tang was then secured to the mast with gap-filling glue. However, as a further precaution a $1\frac{1}{4}$ in. diameter tube was fitted as a through-bolt, and in order to prevent any working in the mast this was bonded into a piece of spruce with Redux, which was then fixed into the mast with gap-filling glue.

It is a sound principle of rigging to avoid shackles aloft wherever possible. The extent to which they may be eliminated depends on the design of the mast tangs and the methods of attachment of the various rigging members. In modern practice, with forked fittings carrying bolts for the upper end of the standing rigging, there is rarely need for shackles, and one source of rigging failure is removed. One is still however left with the split pins of the bolts. They are a small detail in the total rigging assembly; they should carry no stress; and with reasonable care ought to give no trouble: but a small carelessness and the loss of a split pin could take the mast out of a ship. There has been a case of a shroud hanging on its bolt, which has lost both pin and nut, and fortunately remaining in position (for how long one does not know) retained there by the tension in the shroud. How easily it might not have done so.

Chainplates.—On a visit to one of the largest South Coast yards lately I made a rough proportion of the various types of chainplates fitted in the yachts which were there. It was surprising to find what a high proportion of the craft had the old fashion, external strap chainplates (*Fig. 39 (a)*) and many boats had this type bent outboard over channels to increase the spread of the rigging, and in cases where it looked hardly necessary (*Fig. 39 (b)*). Such an arrangement was once, of course, very common, and in the days of extremely narrow beam was the only way of obtaining sufficient spread of shrouds to support the mast. Even certain of the J-class had channels; but we may be satisfied that in no yacht of reasonable proportions will they be necessary to-day.

The importance of strength in the chainplates is indicated in Lloyd's rules by the fact that the Society, which encourages yellow metal fastenings everywhere else, readily

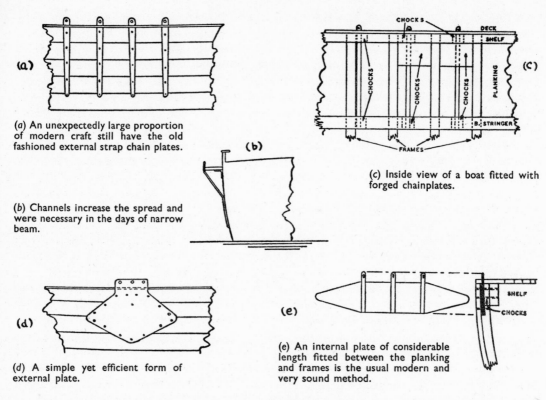

(a) An unexpectedly large proportion of modern craft still have the old fashioned external strap chain plates.

(b) Channels increase the spread and were necessary in the days of narrow beam.

(c) Inside view of a boat fitted with forged chainplates.

(d) A simple yet efficient form of external plate.

(e) An internal plate of considerable length fitted between the planking and frames is the usual modern and very sound method.

Figure 39.—Chainplates.

accepts galvanised steel bolts in these fittings on account of their greater strength. Stainless steel or monel bolts would doubtless be best of all, but galvanised steel is certainly likely to be superior to the various dubious alloys which pass under the name of naval brass.

The two essential features of chainplates are that they should be strong enough to carry the rigging loads which are put in them, and that these loads should be distributed over the hull sufficiently widely to prevent any deformation of structure. Many people, myself included, have known chainplates to break at sea owing to faulty forging or poor metal; and everyone has at some time seen boats, particularly older ones, with hogged sheerlines in the way of their standing rigging, resulting from the stresses being too concentrated, or from a hull construction which is too light in way of the chainplates to carry the loads.

External chainplates, apart from their ugliness, add slightly to the resistance of the hull, and in first-class work to-day they are fitted internally, passing through the covering board and fitting against the inside of the planking. When simple forged straps are used, the principles of fitting are similar whether the straps are internal or external.

Fig. 39 (c) shows a view inside a boat fitted with three forged strap chainplates. Ideally the straps should be fitted closely against the frames, where the support to the planking is strongest, and the straps should extend down to the bilge stringer. For some reason the stock chainplates of marine hardware dealers are always absurdly short and special fittings may have to be made to suit the individual case. It will be seen that the chainplates pass between the planking and the deck shelf and bilge stringer. At both these points there should be chocks on top of the straps and the straps should be bolted through them and the planking and the shelf or stringer. Then the rigging stresses are distributed through the longitudinal members of the frame and not carried simply in the planking.

The line of each chainplate should follow that of the shroud which it carries, thus ensuring that only tensile stresses fall on the strap. The lead of the shrouds is governed by consideration of rig, and usually the position of the chainplates imposed thus will not allow their ideal placing in relation to the frames. When the chainplate has to be fitted in the bay between frames more elaborate chocking is necessary. Then the entire bay should be chocked, the piece of timber fitting *hard against the lower edge of the deck shelf*, on top of the chainplate, the bolts passing through planking, chock and chainplate. By this means the stresses are distributed and the planking stiffened where it is without the support of a frame.

Though many of the most modern and best designed yachts use chainplates of this type, ones embodying a metal plate are now often adopted, this distributing the stresses more widely over the hull structure. The simplest form is merely an external metal plate bolted through the planking, with chocking arranged on the principles indicated above (*Fig. 39 (d)*). But more usually now the plate is internal, of considerable length, and with forged straps riveted to it. It is fitted between the frames and the planking, the frames being checked in way of the plate so that it is flush with the moulded line of the frames. The planking is laid over the plate, and there is chocking between the plate and the deck shelf. The forged straps are riveted on the inside of the plate and pass through the usual water-tight collar or caulking at the covering board (*Fig. 39 (e)*).

The following is a guide to suitable proportions for this plate in craft of various lengths:

L.O.A.	Length of Plate	Depth of Plate
45 ft.	6 ft.	1 ft. 2 in.
50 ft.	7 ft.	1 ft. 4 in.
55 ft.	8 ft.	1 ft. 6 in.
60 ft.	9 ft.	1 ft. 8 in.

Below 45 ft. overall the simple strap chainplate, carried well down the hull, is adequate, and in fact the type is used in the largest craft. But the above arrangement is preferable.

By this means the rigging stresses are spread fore and aft through the deck shelf and also, by means of the chocking, through the frames. The length of the straps may therefore be reduced and made no more than the depth of the plate. A neater and more effective distribution of material is achieved than with the long, independent strap chainplates extending to the bilge stringer. A further distribution of the stresses is obtained where the plate passes through bulkheads, the plate being fastened to these by angle brackets.

In smaller racing craft internal chainplates are now sometimes fitted, the shrouds, whether rod or wire, passing through the covering board to rigging screws arranged below the deck. This may be seen in the 5.5-Metre in Plates 41 and 42.

13

LEVERS AND WINCHES

Levers.—Much ingenuity has been devoted to the gear used for handling the runners, and whether or not a yacht is good to windward and easily handled depends to a big extent on the efficiency of this gear. The problem is this: to provide the means of putting the high tension in the runners which they need to support forestays carrying modern, efficient headsails, and at the same time to enable this gear to be handled quickly and without confusion under the often difficult conditions of tacking and gybing, or when sailing at night.

The gear now used for this purpose falls into five categories: (i) Tackles; (ii) Slides; (iii) Levers; (iv) Winches; (v) Various combinations of these.

Tackles, unassisted by winches, are the inheritance of the past and have many disadvantages. In craft of any size the purchase has to be a powerful one, and hence of many parts. When letting the runner go a great length of rope has to be overhauled through the blocks, with the incidental probability that it will twist and complicate the operation of setting up the purchase again later.

When tackles are used in combination with winches the purchases may be simpler and more easily handled. *Fig. 40* shows a purchase and winch system in which is embodied a release hook allowing the runner to be carried forward to the shrouds, when the boom is squared off, without the need for overhauling the purchase. The upper block of the purchase has a heavy hook carrying the runner. The fall of the purchase, from the lower block, is led forward or aft to a winch. When letting go the runner the purchase is eased enough to allow the hook to be released. The purchase is then laid on deck, and the runner brought forward and secured with a clip to the shrouds. A light line is secured to the lower end of the runner to guard against losing it aloft. The hook in this arrangement needs careful design. Its important dimension is depth, not breadth. It should be narrow enough to make a snug fit on the thimble of the runner, and deep enough to prevent any tendency for the eye in the runner to jump off it. The extreme end of the hook may then be opened out to facilitate its engagement. In practice, with a deep hook and the weight of the purchase helping to hold it securely in position, no tendency has been found for the hook to become detached accidentally, even when the tackle is eased and the runner allowed to sag forward a little to clear the belly of the mainsail when close hauled.

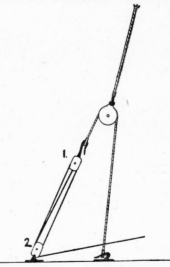

Figure 40.—A runner arrangement incorporating a purchase of power five with the fall led to a winch. This is suitable for craft of 40 tons or more. The hook on the upper block of the purchase allows the purchase to be released from the runner fall when easing the runner forward, obviating the need to overhaul a long length of rope.

Another arrangement embodying tackle and winch is shown in *Fig. 41*. The standing end of the runner's wire ship is secured as usual to a deck eyeplate. The hauling part passes over a vertical deck sheave, forward and round an open-ended, flat deck block, and thence aft to the becket of the forward block of the rope purchase. The fall of this purchase is taken to the winch. There is great power in this system, and it will be effective in 20-ton sloops and larger, carrying big Genoas. A certain amount of slack in the runner, equal to twice the distance between the flat and vertical deck blocks, is readily obtained simply by disengaging the wire from the open-ended block.

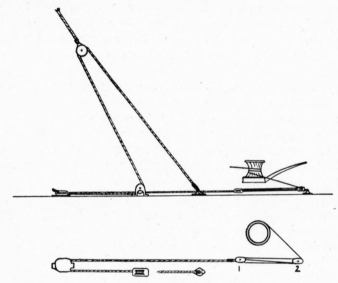

Figure 41.—A runner arrangement incorporating both purchase and winch.

A well proved system of operating the runners in smaller craft is the slide. In its simplest and probably most effective form the slide consists of a wire span, which has to be most securely bolted through the deck and beams at its ends, and on this rides a saddle or bridle shackle carrying the runner (Plate 45). Though in certain highly developed racing classes like the Dragons this system is now replaced by what are regarded as more modern and efficient ones, it is notable that *Circe*, the most successful British 6-Metre during her long day, retained it throughout her life, and a 5.5-Metre which appeared in the 1952 season also sets up her runners in this way. This is the craft in Plate 45. It is very commonly used in small half-decked craft, and may be fitted in large ones also unless the drift of the runners is very big. It will be evident that the power in this system increases as the drift of the runner decreases.

The runner is hauled aft along the span by a line attached near the shackle on the span. A purchase or a winch may be incorporated in the system, but in smaller boats this may cause complication without material advantage. *Circe* had excellent, large barrel American winches installed for this purpose. They were found to be unnecessary, and the runners were always hardened by hand. But in large craft a purchase will be found necessary.

The wire span may be replaced by a metal bar, the runner then riding on a bow shackle, but the preferable alternative, if the wire span is to be discarded, is a length of heavy deck track with the runner riding on a slide. A refinement on this system is a special backstay track engaging a spring-loaded slide which has a quick release device for slacking the runner. Various locking systems have been devised. In one a catch is placed at the point on the track to which the runner is drawn when set up hard, and on this the slide engages. It is important in all such systems that the catch should be certain in action and not capable of being tripped accidentally. Boats have been dismasted from this cause. Devices of this nature are popular in the smaller American racing classes.

Levers have the advantage of making the setting up and releasing of backstays a matter of a single, quick movement, whilst they also ensure that the same tension is put in the stay each time. They now have a fairly long history behind them, and various patterns of lever have appeared. In its original form it was the invention of Mr. J. S. Highfield, who experimented with the device on board his 15-Metre *Dorina*. It consists of a channel bar hinged on the deck and drilled with four holes on either side which allow adjustments to be made in the position of the bolt carrying the runner. In Plate 46 the runner is set up, being hardened at a considerable leverage by the last few inches of movement of the handle. By swinging the lever forward over its hinge the runner is released and an amount of slack is obtained in it equal to twice the distance from the runner bolt to the hinge. This will not be enough for all purposes, and the layout often adopted with this type of lever is shown in *Fig. 42*. The forward leg of the runner whip is hooked into a deck eyeplate, and the after leg passes over a deck block to the lever. (This part of the runner gear may be seen also in Plate 26.) When more slack is wanted the hook is released.

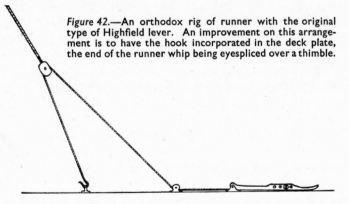

Figure 42.—An orthodox rig of runner with the original type of Highfield lever. An improvement on this arrangement is to have the hook incorporated in the deck plate, the end of the runner whip being eyespliced over a thimble.

It may be noted that the orthodox arrangement is shown in *Fig. 42*. It is a more sensible practice, though one which for some reason is not often adopted, to have the hook on the deck hook plate, the forward leg of the runner whip having an eyesplice over a thimble to engage with it. This eliminates the hazard of having a large hook swinging in the air.

Though this type of lever is still in general use, many improved designs are now available. The original design was improved by Rod Stephens and later by Laurent Giles, and more recently several variations of the lever principle have appeared.

A good, modern layout of lever-operated runner gear is shown in *Fig. 43*. The lever consists not of a channel but of a single bar with a slot along its length, through which rides, on a bolt, a sort of shuttle, into which is screwed a hook carrying the runner. This screw allows the tension in the runner to be adjusted, and more readily than with the system of alternative belt positions in the earlier type of lever. This design also gives more power, for the channel lever, though very powerful during the last inches of its movement, lacks power initially owing to the small leverage. As a result, unless the lever is long it may fail to set up the runner hard enough; or if adjusted to do so may need the weight of someone standing on it to force it down into position. Then the advantage of a lever's convenience is lost.

Figure 43.—A modern runner arrangement, incorporating the Giles type of lever, which, by unhooking from the lever, allows plenty of slack to be obtained in the runner combined with the utmost simplicity of rig.

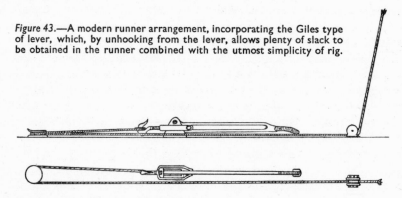

The layout of the gear in *Fig. 43* allows a large amount of slack to be obtained, yet the arrangement is simple. In this case the runner backstay leads direct from the mast to the vertical deck sheave, there being no whip in its lower part. If sufficient leverage can be obtained without one this is an advantage, for it eliminates the block in the air, which can be a danger and a nuisance. The runner leads from the vertical deck block to a flat deck snatch block aft, and forward to the hook on the lever. When the lever is released an amount of slack equal to the length of the lever is obtained. When more is needed the runner is cast off the lever hook, this giving additional slack equal to the distance between the flat snatch block and the vertical deck block, plus a little more which depends on the distance between the lever's hook, when the lever is released, and the snatch block. Since the eyesplice in the runner cannot pass the vertical deck block, the gear has to be laid out so that this slack is sufficient to allow the boom being squared off.

Winches.—Winches, like levers, are a compact mechanical method of obtaining power. To a large extent they have now replaced blocks and tackles, and there are yachts so rigged that there are not more than a couple of tackles on board. Small winches are capable of giving a greater mechanical advantage than complicated, compound purchases, and the power losses in the mechanism are less than those due to the friction in the blocks, sheaves, and parts of a purchase. Winches are easier to operate than purchases, and less likely to become foul, which is a particular danger with purchases having blocks moving aloft. That winches have had the most beneficial effect on the rigging of yachts is certain. To be convinced of this, it is only necessary to consider the well-rigged modern yacht carrying a full equipment of winches, and then to think of the same yacht with all the winches removed, and to picture the fathoms of extra rope, the two part sheets, the python coils of tackles, with which she would have to be cumbered to give her crew equal power to handle the gear.

Winches are not in fact a new piece of gear, though their extensive use in yachts of all sizes is a modern feature of design. And the best winches of the past seem to have been at least as good as the best of the present day. Those designed by Nathaniel G. Herreshoff in 1903 for the *Reliance* were handed down to *Resolute* in 1920, and then to *Enterprise* in 1930. Some of them may even have found their way on board *Ranger* six years later. Winch design, even to-day when nearly every boat down to the smallest dinghy carries a winch, is not one of the strongest features of yacht design. The common failings are winch drums of a shape which cause riding turns in the rope, handles and spindles which are not strong enough for the work which they have to do, and mixtures of metals in the mechanism—especially of light alloy and bronze, a combination which, admittedly, it is not easy to avoid—which cause corrosion. This mixture of metals in most light winches makes careful clearing an important precaution in their maintenance.

Winches may be broadly categorised into two types: (i) Direct Action; (ii) Geared. They may be further subdivided into those operated by a handle fixed at the top of the drum, those having the handle at the bottom, and those which are self-stowing and provide the means of coiling a wire rope as well as the power to haul it.

Direct action winches achieve their effect by the mechanical advantage gained from a small radius drum working in conjunction with a relatively long handle. The mechanical advantage is in proportion to the ratio of handle length and drum radius, and an increase in the former or decrease in the latter gives greater power. The expression is:

$$\frac{\text{Length of handle from centre of drum to hand grip}}{\text{Radius of drum}} = \text{Mechanical Advantage}$$

This sets a limit to the power of such winches. If the barrel is very small the friction between the wire and the barrel is reduced, and unless an inconvenient number of turns of rope are taken round the drum there is danger of slipping. Also, small drums cannot be used with large wire rope (a barrel diameter of ten times the diameter of the wire has been suggested as the minimum acceptable, and more than this is desirable) and small drums tend to cripple the wire. A long handle is an inconvenience and also liable to be weak. These two factors therefore limit the power of direct action winches; which is nevertheless sufficient for the handling of sheets and halyards in small yachts, while direct action winches may be used for halyards in craft of 40 tons or more.

The principle of their action is simple. The handle turns with the drum, both rotating on the same spindle. Internally are two sets of spring loaded pawls, and at the top and bottom of the barrel are circular pawl tracks which allow the drum alone to rotate one way, and the drum and spindle the other. The familiar clicking of winches is the sound of the pawls running over the teeth of the pawl tracks. The direction of rotation when winding in is unfortunately not standardised though clockwise is the usual arrangement, which means that the turns of rope are also taken clockwise round the drum. Sometimes the winches on the port and starboard side of a yacht turn in different directions, and then an arrow painted on the deck is the only way to guard against confusion when handling them.

The second type of winch gains its power by internal gearing, and several advantages, especially applicable to sheet winches, follow from this. Large diameter drums may be used, these giving greater control of the wire rope, and allowing sufficient friction to be obtained between the wire and the drum to hold the load with only a few turns of wire round the drum. Handles may also be conveniently short. A further refinement is possible; such winches may have two gears, the change of gear being effected either by a small lever or, in some designs, by reversing the direction of rotation of the handle. Then, usually, the winch operates in high gear when rotating clockwise, and the final hardening of the sheet is done with the lower gear whilst rotating the handle anti-clockwise.

A critical feature of the design of winches is the shape of the barrel. It has to allow the rope to wind easily on to and off the drum without any tendency to cause the turns to ride on top of one another. Some winches are bad in this respect, some are good, and it is not always easy to decide why. All winch drums have a flange at the top to retain the turns of rope on the barrel. Usually drums have a radiused section (Plates 46 and 47) to encourage the turns to remain near the centre of the drum; but too sharp a radius produces riding turns, and winches with flat sided drums (Plates 49 and 50) are sometimes the most satisfactory. There are winches which are flat sided but with a taper towards the bottom of the drum, the diameter being smaller here than at the top. Others have a taper the other way, and these at least seem definitely dangerous. The balance of advantage would seem to lie with the flat sided barrel or those with a slight, uniform radius.

To increase the friction between the drum and rope and prevent slipping hexagonal drums are used (Plate 46) or whelps may be fitted to circular ones (Plate 47), these consisting of narrow strips of metal or Tufnol attached round the circumference of the drum. A subtle compromise has to be attained here between a drum which is too small or smooth to offer enough friction, and whelps which may offer so much that the veering of a sheet becomes a difficult, and even dangerous, operation.

Direct action winches may be operated by a handle at the top or bottom of the barrel. On the whole the former is to be preferred. With this type the turns of the sheet or halyard have to be taken round the drum before the handle is inserted. An important element in the efficiency of a winch is the ease with which the handle may be engaged, and its security when in position. Bottom handle winches allow the rope turns to be made whilst the handle is in position, but the handle easily fouls the sheet. Geared winches sometimes have a chain drive connection between the handle and the winch itself, when the handle may be separated by a few feet from the barrel, which makes the operation of the winch easier for all concerned. The most elaborate winch of this kind is the American pedestal type, which has double handles rotating vertically on a pedestal situated well clear of the drum; but this is suitable only for large craft. Geared winches with bottom handles on a long spindle for operating below the deck are the best design for the headsail sheet winches of small half-decked racers (Plate 50). They are unsuitable for fully decked craft. The pattern illustrated, fitted on board a 5.5-Metre, is of Sparkman and Stephens design and made of light alloy. The drum of large diameter will be noticed.

A new type of two-speed winch has recently come on the market, which was invented and patented by Mr. C. Smallpeice, a keen racing yachtsman with many inventions to his credit. He found that normal winches were either too slow or not powerful enough for his 8-metre Cruiser/Racer, after which the winches have been named " C.R." Cam operated the basic principle is extremely simple: the lever is pivoted eccentric to the winch; thus one end, that for high speed, impacts a greater angular movement to the drum than the other for low gear. Gear changing can only be effected at the beginning of the stroke, but not a split second is lost in doing this. Another advance on previous designs of winches is the elimination of internal gear wheels. These winches have salt-water resisting light alloy drums, and nickel-aluminium bronze is used for the other parts. The standard size has a mechanical advantage of $15 : 1$ on low gear and $3\frac{3}{4} : 1$ on high gear, but they are made in three sizes, and are marketed by Camper and Nicholsons Ltd.

Self-stowing winches which coil the halyard on the drum are a great convenience for main halyards, and have been used satisfactorily for headsail halyards. Hard things have been said about this type of winch, but when of good design they have proved to be remarkably trouble-free, and they make the operation of hoisting and lowering the mainsail altogether simpler. The important requirements in self-stowing winches are: (i) the drum must be of sufficient size to accommodate the length and size of halyard needed; (ii) the power must be high enough to hoist the sail comfortably, allowance being made for the loss in mechanical advantage as the drum increases in virtual diameter with coils of the halyard. It is unfortunate that the latter results in winches of this type becoming progressively less powerful as the need for power becomes greater—as the sail nears the top of the hoist; (iii) there must be a brake mechanism on the drum, allowing the sail to be lowered gently. Experience with self-stowing winches has proved that they are capable of stowing their halyards neatly and without fouling, and danger of snarls occurs only if sudden, excessive slack is allowed to come into the halyard when lowering.

Winches of this type usually have direct action mechanism, and are retained from running back while hoisting by a ratchet, which has to be released when lowering. In a pattern of winch made by Messrs. Merriman the ratchet is eliminated, its place being taken by a band brake actuated by a differential lever, which comes automatically into action if the drum tries to turn in the anti-clockwise direction (Plates 50 (a) and (b). The brake is released by the handle at the top in Plate 50, but the band maintains enough friction on the drum to control the lowering of the sail. The following drum capacities for three sizes of wire halyard, which are applicable to this winch, will serve as a general guide:

Drum Diameter $2\frac{3}{8}$ in.

$\frac{1}{2}$ in. circ. wire	88 ft.
$\frac{5}{8}$ in. circ. wire	62 ft.
$\frac{3}{4}$ in. circ. wire	45 ft.

Various patterns of winch, including several self-stowing halyard winches, are shown in Plates 48, 49, 50, 52, 53, 55 and 56.

Self-stowing winches may be used for headsails. It is sometimes claimed that there is greater likelihood of getting a riding turn of wire on the drum when they are used for headsails, this being the result of the initial slackness in the halyard when hoisting. They have, nevertheless, been used extensively in yachts for this purpose, though it is more common in American than English craft. A battery of self-stowing halyard winches is shown in Plate 57, the three winches, of direct action type, being contained in a metal casing on the fore side of the mast. This is the neatest method of handling halyards which has been devised, and has been satisfactorily adopted in craft of 10 tons and even less.

It is important that winches should be placed where they are reasonably easy to operate. Power is wasted if the operators have to kneel or crouch in positions where they can only apply half their strength. The lead of the sheet on to the drum has also to be considered. To avoid riding turns on sheet winches the wire must lead on to the barrel at an angle slightly above the horizontal. If the lead is below the horizontal riding turns are inevitable.

Headsail sheet winches are normally sited outside the cockpit coamings on the port and starboard sides, far enough forward to be clear of the helmsman. At one time they were placed on chocks of hardwood, which were clumsy, and also resulted in a surprising amount of the water on the lee deck breaking against them and depositing itself in the cockpit. Now the winches are secured to rigid metal brackets (Plates 25 and 46). In Plate 47 we see two powerful, geared headsail sheet winches placed inside the cockpit coaming. The cockpit is a small one of the foot-bath variety, and inevitably there is a certain congestion, the winches being very close to the tiller and helmsman. Geared winches are heavy and expensive pieces of equipment, and it is economical in money, weight, and space in the cockpit, if a single winch can be sited to serve both port and starboard sheets. The counter is usually the place for such a winch (Plate 51). The headsail sheets are then led from the appropriate bonnet on the deck track to a block in the covering board on the quarter placed so as to give a fair lead on to the central winch. In large cutters this winch will handle the Genoa and the Yankee and smaller jibs, while the staysail sheets are controlled by winches on either side of the cockpit or on the deck forward.

The siting of a mainsheet winch is often difficult. A bridge deck helps to solve this problem, and in Plate 47 the mainsheet winch may be seen placed on the middle line, with the two falls of the double-ended mainsheet rove through quarter blocks at the port and starboard coamings. In small craft with open cockpits it is usually convenient to lead the mainsheet forward of the helmsman. A vertically acting winch may then be fitted on sampson post amidships (Plate 18). In all craft the siting of the winches is an individual matter depending on the details of the layout. The quality to be sought is ease of operation under all circumstances.

There is perhaps a danger to-day, in spite of the terrifying price of winches, of spoiling the beautiful simplicity of the modern rig by using two winches where one will serve, and then even adding a few unnecessary purchases as well—the latter perhaps as a concession to the Old Guard.

If, for example, we install mast halyard winches for the staysail and jib, why should there also be tack winches or tackles for these two sails on the deck forward? The only result is to make two processes necessary when hoisting the sail when one will serve equally well. First we have to set up on the mast winch, belay, then go forward and kneel on a particularly wet and bouncing piece of deck and set up the tack on an awkwardly placed and awkward-to-work ratchet winch. It is difficult to see what is gained by this procedure. Either the mast winches or the deck winches are redundant, and obviously the ones to retain are those on the mast, which are at a convenient height to work efficiently and in a reasonably dry part of the ship.

In yachts of even 5 tons and under one sees main halyard winches in combination with two-part main halyards when, using the winch, a single-part halyard would suffice. Either the two parts or the winch is redundant. All that the tackle on the main halyard does is to make the initial hoisting of the mainsail unnecessarily slow, twice the amount of rope having to be overhauled, whilst the block fouls the mast fittings and jumper struts on the way up and again, more dangerously, when lowering.

The use of a downhaul under the boom as well as a main halyard winch on the mast is reasonable in large craft for, for some not perfectly clear reason, the load in the masthead from the halyard does seem to be lessened if the final setting up of the sail is done by the downhaul rather than the hard winching of the halyard itself. But this is hardly applicable to small craft.

The only other argument I have heard for this arrangement is that by using a downhaul the weight of the boom is added to the operator's efforts to get a straight luff. Surely this is muddled thinking? Before the boom can be hauled down—a process greatly assisted I agree by its own weight—it has to be lifted up. In small yachts this may be done single handed using the main halyard winch, though a little further encouragement is generally needed to persuade the boom to slide properly on its track. We often see a number of the crew sweating with their shoulders under the boom helping the hand on the winch to lift the boom *and all for the pleasure of hauling it down again* on the downhaul. Why not have a fixed gooseneck and expend the energy initially on hardening the luff by means of the main halyard winch? One cannot get anything for nothing in mechanics.

14

GOOSENECKS AND ROLLER REEFING

THE old, bad type of gooseneck had a single, narrow band clamped round the mast. Its bearing surface on the mast was small, and on round masts it tended either to slip, or if clamped tightly enough to prevent this, to crush the wood. The boom was pivoted on a pin held below the point of pivot, and with no support above it. It is a type of gooseneck still sometimes found amongst the cheap hardware offered for small boats.

An improved version of this basic type of gooseneck is shown in Plate 62. The obvious weaknesses have been eliminated. The gooseneck is clamped to the mast by two bands, and the pivot is supported top and bottom, thereby distributing the shear stresses, which may be considerable in a seaway, between both ends of the pin. A further improvement in the design, originated I think by Claud Worth, is to have a thin, steel plate (in two halves like the bands) and riveted inside them. This gives a large bearing surface of metal on the mast, and the increase in friction allows the clamping to be less hard, whilst the pressure is spread over a big area of wood. It is possible to have the same sort of pivot pin as the above when a single mast band is used. Then lugs are forged at the top and bottom of the band to carry the ends of the pin.

Nowadays, with oval and box masts, gooseneck bands do not always encircle the mast, and the fastening to the mast is by screwing (Plates 63 and 64). Sometimes the mast attachment is an almost flat plate carrying no more than eight or ten fastenings. Though it has proved satisfactory for mizzen booms, a heavier fitting would be needed for a mainboom.

In Plate 62 it will be seen that the gooseneck fitting combines the lugs and bolt for the tack cringle of the sail. Usually the distance between the bolt and the mast produces an unfair lead for the sail from the mast track. A clumsy way of obviating this is to lace the bottom few feet of the luff to the mast. When roller reefing is fitted the separation between the mast and tack bolt is inevitably greater, owing to the space occupied by the gear, and simultaneously the need for a perfectly fair lead for the luff of the sail becomes more important if the luff rope is not to become fouled when rolling round the boom. In all cases where the tack bolt and the mast are widely separated the mast track should be carried, for its last few feet, on a tapered spline wide enough at the bottom to bring the end of the track and the tack bolt close together. This is essential with roller reefing and desirable anyhow (Plate 63).

Sliding goosenecks are now usual, the gooseneck running in a length of track on the mast. In larger craft the track must be very heavy (Plate 64), and the T-bar rather than channel section may be used. If of light alloy the reinforced channel section with side fastenings, of the sort made by Messrs. James Gibbons Ltd., may be fitted. The luff of the mainsail is then hardened by means of a downhaul tackle under the gooseneck (Plate 64).

The advantages* which may be claimed of this system are that the final setting up of the main halyard is facilitated, and that perhaps the stresses in the masthead are slightly reduced by taking the final weight in the downhaul instead of winching directly on the main halyard. A sliding gooseneck also allows a measure of sail shortening to be achieved simply by easing the halyard and letting the boom drop to the bottom of the slide.

The following lengths of slide are suggested:

Mainsail Area	Length of Slide
300 sq. ft.	18 in.
500 sq. ft.	24 in.
800 sq. ft.	27 in.
1,000 sq. ft.	30 in.
1,500 sq. ft.	36 in.

All roller reefing gears have faults, and the best that anyone can do in choosing a pattern is to decide which faults he prefers to live with. The well-known Turner roller reefing gear consists basically of a lever handle operating on a ratchet, and a pawl which also engages the ratchet and prevents the boom from turning when the sail is reefed. The worm gear, which was used on the Bristol Channel Pilot Cutters and which is known also as the Appledore type, is the stronger gear and less likely to give trouble. It consists (Plate 65) of a worm operated by a rotating handle and engaging in a pinion on the boom.

The Turner ratchet gear is potentially more efficient than the latter, for the power losses in a worm and pinion are high. It is also a lighter gear, and for this reason more suitable for small craft. But it is liable to jam, and it is often difficult to release the pawl when the time comes to shake out a reef. The pawl itself is a source of weakness. Both the Appledore and the Turner gears carry heavy twisting stresses when a reef has been taken and the sail no longer leads from the middle of the boom, and in both gears this is a potential cause of failure. The stresses are carried in the pawl of the Turner gear, and it and its pin have to be of great strength. Failure of the pawl is not uncommon. The boom then releases itself violently and shakes out the reef without warning.

There are however yachtsmen of experience who prefer the ratchet to the worm gear. Humphrey Barton is one, and he fitted the Turner pattern in *Vertue XXXV* and tested it highly on his Atlantic crossing. When discussing the reefing question with him he stressed, in favour of the Turner method, the fact that the lever handle may be long, giving the operator plenty of power; whereas in the worm gear the rotating handle is often too small and not only fouls the sail after a few rolls have been taken in it, but may even lack the power to turn the boom when it is bending slightly in a weight of wind. A

* *For disadvantages see page* 155.

L

small handle, however, is an unnecessary fault. On one yacht I discovered accidentally that the handle of the anchor winch fitted the reefing gear, and very much more effective it was than the proper, small handle.

There are various other types of reefing gear. Claud Worth's pattern, like the Turner, works on the ratchet principle, but means are provided of relieving the gooseneck of twisting stresses. In the wire and drum system the twisting stress is again taken out of the gooseneck. It is carried in the wire which is wound round a drum at the heel of the boom. This wire, led to a suitable winch, is the means of rotating the boom. Complicated mechanical reefing methods such as these have tended to lose their place in modern yachts with their short and relatively light booms; but very small patterns of the wire and drum gear, with the wire replaced by a length of light line, are suitable for dinghies and half-decked boats.

An important part of any roller-reefing gear is the fitting at the outer end of the boom. Excluding claw rings, which are unnecessary with the short booms of to-day, these are of two types (Plates 66 and 68). The former consists of a pivoted arm to one end of which is shackled the topping lift and to the other the main sheet. The stronger and better fitting is that of Plate 68, consisting of a revolving band riding in a metal collar at the end of the boom and carrying the sheet and lift attachments. This design eliminates the bending stresses which fall in the long and often insufficiently strong arm of the other fitting.

A roller reefing boom has to be more or less circular, and may not be encumbered with gear—which means that outhauls must be simplified and topping lifts be led down the mast. Ideally, too, the track should be recessed into the boom, as in Plate 65. Unless steps are taken to prevent it a roller reefing boom will droop at its outer end as the canvas winds on to the spar. This is caused by the increase in the virtual diameter of the boom near the heel when the mainsail's bulky luff rope, and the slides too, pile up round the boom. A roller boom has therefore to be tapered to a reduced diameter towards the heel to allow for this. There is one school of thought which insists that the best setting reefed mainsail is obtained if the after half of the boom's length is parallel, and the taper is taken off the forward half only, this allowing any slackness in the bunt of the mainsail to be taken up in the rolls. Instead of tapering the boom, a method often adopted to achieve the same result is to fit long, tapered splines on the boom, these being an inch to an inch and a half deep at the outer end of the boom, and running off to nothing at about its mid length; though it is better if the splines extend for about three-quarters of the boom's length.

There is a pattern of reefing gear made by Merriman in the U.S.A. the principle of which is shown in *Fig. 44*. Its object is to eliminate the drooping of the boom without tapering it or resorting to splines. It does this by disposing neatly of the rolled length of the luff rope. The gear is of the worm type with the mechanism enclosed and guarded to prevent fouling and chafe. The best British patterns now have enclosed mechanism. The crucial features in the Merriman gear are firstly the neck in the metal boom socket, and secondly the special type of shackles used for attaching the lower slides to the luff of the mainsail. The neck gives a certain length, between the boom end and the mainsail tack shackle, of reduced diameter into which the luff rope feeds without increasing the boom's virtual diameter. The shackles of the lower slides have quick-release drop-pins, allowing the sail to be detached readily from the slides, thus leaving the luff rope clear for reeling neatly into the neck.

The question of whether or not to fit roller reefing is not always easy to answer. It is more desirable in boats which have a tendency to need reefing often, due to inherent tenderness in the hull or a big mainsail, than in stiffer craft with small mainsails. And it is more likely to justify itself in the under-manned cruiser than in an ocean racer carrying a large and competent crew.

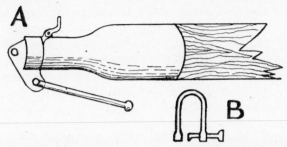

Figure 44.—Worm roller reefing gear with enclosed mechanism and reduced diameter at gooseneck to take the rolled luff rope.

15

MAST TRACKS AND SLIDES

THE Bermudian rig became possible only with the development of tracks and slides for the mainsail. We may therefore say that the modern, easily handled and efficient rig of yachts is due to the development of these two fittings.

The potted history of the track and slides in relation to the Bermudian rig is this: The tall, narrow sail plan is practicable only when tall hollow masts can be used, and such masts cannot be kept upright and reasonably straight unless they are split up, for staying purposes, into a number of short panels by spreaders, which reduce the unsupported length of the mast and allow a good angle of spread to be obtained for the shrouds. But spreaders can be used only if the mechanism for attaching the sail to the mast does not, like mast hoops, embrace the mast. Hence tracks and slides, which were first used more than a century ago, before the *America* was thought of, but which are still being developed and improved.

Certainly the early and many more recent tracks and slides were bad, and these fittings did more than anything else to damn the Bermudian rig for sea-going. The jamming of mainsails aloft owing to faulty track mechanism led to numerous dangerous situations, and even to-day an argument used against the Bermudian rig is the difficulty of lowering the mainsail without luffing. In fact, with the right track and slides, a mainsail may be lowered when full of wind, but it is true that this is not always easy with many of the tracks found in yachts. These fittings still present one of the more complicated and interesting problems in design.

The essence of the problem is this: The track is a rail or tramway made up of a number of lengths, and hence with a number of joints, which has to provide a smooth sliding surface when fixed to the flexible wooden column of the mast. It has to be capable of withstanding such high wringing stresses as come upon it when a mainsail is slatting in a hard wind without deforming or drawing its fastenings and hence losing its fairness. And since its weight is high in the ship, this should be as light as the provision of adequate strength will allow.

The chief design problems involved are:

 (i) The shape of the track.
 (ii) The shape of the slide.
(iii) The fastening of the track to the mast.
(iv) The attachment of the slides to the sail.

It is interesting to note the different answer which has been arrived at to the same problem in England and America. I believe that the first tracks in England were of the internal variety—that is, internal relative to the slide, which ran along the outside of them (*Fig. 45 (i), (ii), (iii), (iv)* and *(xii)*). This is the type still used, almost to the exclusion of all others, in the U.S.A. In England the external or channel-section track became popular, and to-day the other sort is rarely seen, though perhaps more often than is the channel-type in American yachts. (*Fig. 45 (v)*, (*vi*) and (*xii*)). There are pros and cons for each type, and the reasons for the singularly clean divergence between the two countries is not clear.

The first tracks were made for external slides by Nathaniel Herreshoff, who designed them for use along the booms of large gaff-rigged yachts. Their form was essentially the same as that used to-day in the U.S.A., and occasionally in England. (*Fig. 45 (i)* and (*ii*).) In the smaller sizes—up to about $\frac{3}{4}$ in.—they may be of rolled section as in (*i*), but in the larger sizes the extruded section of (*ii*), which is stiffer and firmer, will be used. In inshore racing craft, where the reduction of mast weight is more important than absolute reliability and resistance to damage, the lighter type may be favoured up to perhaps the $\frac{7}{8}$-in. size.

In large craft, where the size of track needed may be $1\frac{1}{4}$ in. or more, the simple flat bar of bronze, mounted on a hard wood base of width and depth to give clearance to the external type of slide, is often used. Its advantage is to allow a greater thickness of bronze, for a given width of track, with less weight than section (*ii*), and hence to have better resistance to the wringing stresses which try to lift the flanges of the track. In large craft these stresses may be considerable. The solid metal T-section of (*iii*) is too heavy generally for mast work, but is used extensively for deck tracks, and for clew outhaul slides, and sometimes for sliding goosenecks.

The first channel-section track was a brass one fitted in 1928 in the 46-ton Bermudian cutter *Tiercel* designed by W. G. McBryde. The advantage of channel-section tracks using internal slides seems to be their ability to withstand better the wringing stresses put upon them (*Fig. 45 (v)*). The base upon which the track stands is the full width of the back and there is no exposed flange to become dented or twisted. But a disadvantage is the closeness of the screw heads in the track to the bottom of the slides, which introduces complications in the slide design. It will be apparent that in the external tracks of (*i*) and (*ii*) the screws are well clear of the slide as it runs over the raised flanges, and hence a slight loosening of a screw will not cause a jam. In the flat bar type of track the screw situation is similar to that of the channel section, and again allowance has to be made when designing the slide. There is one type of channel-section track in which the middle part of the base of the track is recessed to a small depth, this being let into a groove in the mast. By this means the heads of the screws are kept clear of the sliding surface. Channel tracks are sometimes wholly recessed into the mast, this providing perfect protection for them, which is particularly valuable in the case of light alloy sections.

Bronze and nickel silver are the common materials for tracks in the U.S.A., bronze and light alloy in England. The various English channel-section tracks in light alloy are generally similar to type (*v*), but in those made by Messrs. Gibbons the thickness of the metal may be varied independently of the width of the track, this producing what they call a " reinforced " section. This is valuable when light alloy is concerned, bearing in mind its relative weakness compared with a good bronze.

For larger boats, the light weight of alloy has allowed a singularly good shape of channel track to be developed, in which the rigidity of the track is assured by a very wide base, which simultaneously serves to take the screws, and keeps them clear of the slides (*Fig. 45 (vi)*). This track, made by Gibbons, has great strength and resistance to wringing.

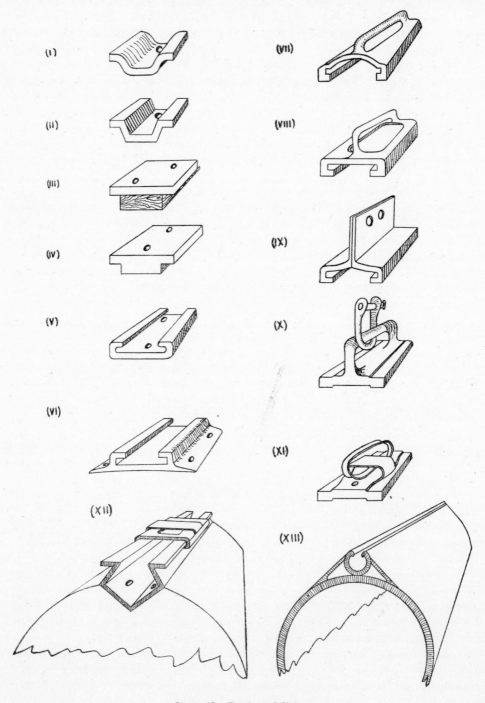

Figure 45.—Tracks and Slides.

Another type of English track in which the problem of fastening is solved in what is also a particularly strong track (it has been adopted by the R.N.L.I.) is that produced by McGruer and shown in *Fig. 45 (xii)*. This has been fitted in several large yachts. Part of its strength is derived from the V–groove in the mast in which the track is fixed, the fastenings being sunk into this groove. This is an internal type of track, but an altogether more rigid and stronger form than that of shape (*ii*). The slide has several refinements which we will consider shortly.

The fixing of the track to the mast is the next problem, and it is accentuated by the flexibility of the mast and the soft wood out of which it is made. The screws should be staggered, their lateral separation being as great as possible—hence the superiority of tracks (*vi*) and (*xii*), particularly of the former, in which the separation of the screws is greater than the working width of the track. It is important that the track should be fair when sighted, and this is helped if it has a hardwood batten under it. This provides a better grip for the screws than spruce, making them less likely to work loose, and also allows them to be hardened down without so much danger of them deforming the track beneath. It is easy, with excessive hardening of the screws in spruce, to produce unfairnesses in a track, and particularly an alloy one. It is also desirable for the butting edges of joints in the track to be rounded off slightly to prevent any proud edges due to slight working.

Slides appear in a variety of shapes. The orthodox external type for use with track of section (*ii*) is shown in *Fig. 106 (viii)*, and a lighter slide of similar type is made for the smaller rolled section of track in (*i*). This type of slide is sometimes suggested for the flat bar track mounted on a hardwood batten, but it is not the best advice since it will readily foul the first screw which works loose. For this purpose the top of the slide should be domed, as in type (*vii*), this also having the effect of reducing the surface friction of the slide on the track. Internal slides for use with channel tracks (*Fig. 45 (x)* and (*xi*)) should also have the central portion of the base recessed or domed, both to reduce friction and avoid screw heads; and within limits the deeper this recess the better.

To ensure smooth running in both external and internal slides, all features which tend to make them trip or cock on the track when weight falls on them lowering or hoisting the sail, must be avoided. Principally this means that the point from which the pull comes on the slide should be as near to its base as possible and as close also to its leading edge as can be arranged—that is, near the top when hoisting and the bottom when lowering. Thus, the type of slide shown in (*ix*), which is to be found in both the internal and external varieties, is bad. The slide is too high relative to its length, and the pull is always concentrated near the middle of the length. Types (*vii*), (*viii*) and (*x*) are admirable in this respect. The longitudinal bar should be no higher above the base of the slide than is needed to pass the shackle, and the latter is free to deliver its pull from the extreme ends of the slide. In this respect, apart from others, a shackle is superior to a lashing, as it is at liberty to travel along the bar and deliver the pull at the best point. The actual length of the slide is another feature which helps to keep it straight on the track, but this has to be limited owing to the formidably combined length of a number of long slides, end to end, when the sail is lowered, which may put the headboard out of reach. In larger yachts this combined length may equal five feet or more.

The simplest way of fastening the slides to the sail luff is by seizing, but the orthodox seizings are so prone to chafe that their replacement can become one of the principal chores on a long passage, particularly offshore in broken water and relatively light winds. Inshore the seizing may be satisfactory enough, and it is lighter and much cheaper than shackles. A type of slide made for secure lashing has been designed by Laurent Giles, and is shown in (xi). The twine passes round a thimble which is integral with a flat cross-bar on the slide. When a sail is slatting, much of the motion is taken in the metal to metal contact of the thimble and slide, and the twisting and chafe of the ordinary slide on its lashing is minimised. Alloy slides of the type (x) are now supplied with shackles in the same metal, which appear to give excellent service. Slides must, of course, be small enough to pass the bar on the slide, but big enough to clear the luff rope, and this is some-times a difficult combination. The slides tend to chafe the luff rope, and this is a serious argument against them. A method of using shackles whilst preventing the friction has been tried in one 10-tonner. The shackles were dipped in molten nylon, which formed a thin skin over the metal, and after two seasons there was no chafe on the luff rope; also, the nylon itself was not rubbed away to any serious extent.

It has long been recognised as one of the disadvantages, aerodynamically, of the track and slide system, that it holds the sail rigidly at the centre of the mast instead of allowing, as did mast hoops, the luff to swing to leeward and clear of mast interference. The slide designed by McGruer for the track already described (xii) is intended to obviate this shortcoming. The sail attachment to the slide rides on a cross-piece which may be equal in width to the slide itself (as shown) or wider than the slide if required, this allowing the luff to ride well to leeward.

Undoubtedly the simplest method of attaching the luff of a mainsail to its mast is by means of running the luff rope in a mast groove. For small, inshore craft, when tracks and slides tend to be rather weak for their weight, the system is justifiably popular, but with wooden masts the grooves are frequently made too narrow, without adequate allowance for the shrinking of the spar, and this results in sticky running and sometimes dangerous situations. And there is also the well-known hazard of varnish fouling the inside of the track with similar results. Both these disadvantages are obviated when the luff grooves are used in combination with alloy masts, the groove being formed by a separate, extruded section fixed to the mast. Many sections are used, and *Fig. 45 (xii)* shows one developed by Reynolds. One disadvantage of the groove system however ap-pears insuperable; this is the difficulty of retaining control of the sail when it runs out of the groove at the bottom, when it generally blows all over the ship. With a groove, it is not possible to fix a stop at the tack; but discounting this disadvantage, grooves have been successfully used in craft of 30 ft. on the waterline and more.

Difficulty is often experienced when feeding the luff into the foot of the groove when the sail is being hoisted. The track should be opened out to form a bell mouth; one method tried with success is to fit a lignum vitae bull's eye at the bottom of the groove, cut through its after side to take the canvas. This makes a smooth entry for the luff rope and sail.

We may complete this survey with what we may call the ideal track and slide. They were designed for *Landfall*, and were refitted on her new masts when the yacht was re-rigged after the war. The track is a very heavy bronze channel, $2\frac{1}{2}$ in. in width and deeply recessed into the mast. It would be difficult to devise a stiffer arrangement. Each slide is a small carriage, complete with four wheels and body, which runs inside the track as smoothly as a model train on its rails. With this track and slides it has always proved possible to lower both mainsail and mizzen with the sail full and in wind forces up to five, and possibly more. Both track and slides are beautiful jobs of engineering. Also expensive ones. When wanting to duplicate these slides for another yacht I found that they would cost a little more than £15 each.

16

SAILS AND THEIR TRIMMING

WE have to consider sail trimming under three different conditions of sailing: when beating to windward; when sailing on a close reach with the apparent wind, as indicated by the burgee, lengths of thread hung in the rigging, or cigarette smoke, lying just free of a dead beat but not abaft the beam; and thirdly when the wind is anywhere between square on the beam and dead astern. Slightly different methods of sail trimming are used in the three cases.

To Windward.—In sailing to windward the first question that has to be answered is " How hard should the mainsail be sheeted ? " It is not easily answered. Consider *Fig. 46* (*a*) and (*b*). In (*a*) the boom is not sheeted in hard but is being carried, as a great many of the smaller, bulkier cruisers like it, a little started. If now we harden the sheet we can sail closer to the wind without altering the angle of incidence of the wind on the sail (*b*) but the amount of useful driving force which may be derived from the sail is now less.

As a result of hardening the mainsheet, the resultant drive from the sail is more nearly square to the fore and aft centreline; so the resolved component of this force along the centreline is smaller and the lateral component, causing heel and leeway, is greater. On the other hand, sailing closer to the wind, the distance which must be sailed to get to a point dead to windward will be less. The boat will be slightly slower, make slightly more leeway, but have to travel slightly less distance.

A balance of advantage has thus to be struck between the reduced speed and the shorter distance to be sailed. If, for example, hardening the sheets results in excessive loss in speed and increase in leeway (if the boat points higher but ceases to foot fast and falls off to leeward) the right balance has not been struck.

How hard a boat will stand having her mainsheet pinned in depends on the ability of the hull to withstand the greater leeway and heeling forces engendered and to maintain a good speed in spite of the reduced effective driving force. It depends, in fact, on the stiffness of the boat, the efficiency of the keel, and the easily driven qualities in the hull lines.

Thus the 6-Metre, or the deep-draft, light displacement ocean racer of narrow beam, will stand the mainsheet pinned in much harder than the average small cruiser with coarser hull lines and relatively inefficient keel. The 6-Metre eats her way to windward with the mainsail pinned almost amidships; the smaller cruiser under such conditions would sag away to leeward and lose her speed.

A factor which controls the trim of the mainsail is the mainsheet horse along which the deck block of the sheet travels. The object of a horse is to control the mainsail's twist. If the sheet leads vertically down to the deck from the boom end when the sail is trimmed, a maximum tension will be put in the leech of the sail and the twist will be reduced. This is to be desired, and particularly so when sailing hard on the wind. The width of the horse is therefore governed by the type of boat. When it is possible to sail with the mainsail hardened in almost on the centreline a very short horse may be used. Sometimes, though it is not ideal, a single eyebolt on the centreline is employed.

In the average small cruiser, when it does not pay to harden in the boom excessively, a wider horse or deck track should be fitted. Ideally the length of horse should be adjustable by means of stops. Then the length may be reduced when beating to windward and the stops moved out when the sheet is eased, this allowing the maximum tension to be maintained in the leech of the sail when close reaching. When broad reaching the stops are put far out along the track.

The stops also allow a finer trim of the sail to be made in different wind strengths. In hard winds, beating to windward, the stops are more widely separated, allowing the sheet to be started a little whilst keeping the sail flat. In light winds the flow in the sail is increased by sheeting it nearer the centreline.

The Headsails when Beating.—The same principles apply to Genoas and smaller staysails, and to both staysails and jibs in cutters, but the sails are boomless and more attention must be paid to the sheet leads. The true Genoa is intended for windward work. It has to be trimmed very flat and, as we have seen, for the best results the block for the deck sheet lead must be fixed on an adjustable bonnet sliding in a length of deck track.

Alternatively there may be several eyebolts in the deck allowing various fore and aft and transverse positions of the lead to be adopted. The position to be used under any condition may be judged by the manner in which the sail lifts as the wind is brought too far forward to keep it full and drawing. If the luff of the sail begins to quiver near the head whilst the lower part of the sail is drawing well, the lead is too far aft; if it is the lower part of the luff which shivers first the lead is too far forward. When the whole length of the luff from foot to clew lifts simultaneously the lead is right.

The reason for these phenomena will be apparent if it is remembered that the fore and aft positions of sheet lead governs the relationship between the tension which the sheet puts in the leech and the foot of the sail. When the lead is well forward the greatest pull is down on the leech; this reduces the twist of the sail: when aft it flattens the foot but allows more twist. This fact has also to be made use of when trimming for different wind strengths. In light weather the sheet leads should be well aft to put flow into the headsails; in harder winds they should be moved forward to flatten the sails.

One point must here be noticed which modifies our method of trimming the mainsail. With Genoas, and even with No. 1 jibs, the mainsail will be backwinded by the headsail and will probably be lifting along the whole length of the luff. For various reasons it pays to trim the Genoa or jib as hard as experience has indicated that the boat likes it and to neglect the lifting of the mainsail, which should be trimmed to about the same angle as the jib and then left to its own devices.

This, of course, is not in accordance with the " slot effect " theory, which under the influence of Manfred Curry for a long time carried great influence. This theory may be explained in the following terms: One of the well-known theorems of physics is that of Bernoulli concerning fluid flow, which shows that if a stream of incompressible fluid passes through a constricted throat or narrowing passage, the rate of flow of the stream increases and the pressure is reduced. If we imagine water flowing full bore along a pipe which narrows to a neck, the velocity of the water will increase at the neck and its pressure decrease. For water substitute air, and for the neck of the pipe substitute the narrowing slot into which the wind is canalised between the overlapping jib and the mainsail, and the slot theory is revealed, though not quite in Curry's manner.

Unfortunately, with unstiffened sails, and overlapping headsails sheeted to the hull itself, it is not possible to arrange an effective slot. Curry, in his fully developed argument, showed that for the development of the slot effect there were certain requirements, the most important of which were fully battened sails and a lead for the Genoa sheet involving outriggers; and both of these are illegal or impracticable in racing and cruising yachts. As a result, the efficiency of Genoa jibs has nothing to do with slot effects, Bernoulli, or the guiding of the air-flow over the leeward surface of the mainsail. Crouch on the bilge stringer of a 6-Metre as she thrashes her way up the windward leg of a course and watch the Genoa, sheeted hard against the lower shrouds and pulling with tremendous strength; then look at the mainsail slatting wildly in its backwind like a flag. How often does every yachtsman see this in all types of boat? This vicious backwinding has nothing to do with slot effects and reduction in pressure. It is the reverse.

One of the most important features in the efficient setting of a headsail is, of course, the straight luff, and the efforts to obtain this have had a great influence on the rigging and the design of modern yachts. The bar-taut rigging which has become fashionable is mainly the result of endeavours to obtain straight forestays, for if the mast bends or sags forward the movement is immediately reflected in a sagging forestay.

When this happens the shape of the headsail is spoilt, the curved luff throwing excessive flow into the sail; and unfortunately the sag in a forestay increases with the wind strength, while the desirable amount of flow in the sail should be decreased under these conditions. The lead of the sail's sheet is also adversely affected. When a forestay curves to leeward, successive points along the luff of the sail above the tack are thrown progressively farther to leeward in the lower half of the luff. But the position of the sheet lead cannot be moved farther outboard than the maximum beam of the boat, and with a Genoa, under even ideal conditions, this is probably not enough for the perfect setting of the sail. With the luff sagging to leeward the condition is aggravated, and a chord of the sail at about the mid-point of the luff lies at a greater angle of incidence to the wind than chords above or below this point. The result is a bigger leeward component of the wind force, and, owing to the smaller angle of the chord to the centreline of the yacht, a more violent back-winding of the mainsail.

Yachts with rigging which is unable to carry the headsail loads or to retain reasonable straightness in the mast find themselves sagging off to leeward in a rising wind under Genoa, and are forced to lower the sail, before the yacht has lost the power and stability to carry it. The source of the trouble is a slack forestay. It should be added, however, that a perfectly straight forestay is unobtainable in any yacht; it is a matter of the degree of sag, and the less there is the better.

Close Reaching.—The essence of sail trimming when close reaching may be resolved into two fundamentals:

> (i) A sail should be kept drawing—that is, full of wind, or as older sailors used to call it, " asleep."

(ii) The sheet should be started, or eased off, as far as the fulfilment of (i) will allow—that is, the sail should be as nearly square to the fore and aft line of the boat as possible, since this is the direction in which we want her to move.

First, considering (i), a sail can only drive a boat by producing a resultant force derived from wind pressures acting on its two surfaces. Approximately we may say that on the windward surface the sail pressures are high and on the leeward surface they are low. When a sail starts lifting or fluttering there is no resultant force being developed from the area of canvas thus affected (it may be part of the sail or the whole sail). The air pressures on both sides of the canvas are roughly equal; hence the lifting of the canvas. Such a state is caused when the angle of the sail to the wind is too small; the angle must be increased.

But the question then arises: How much should it be increased? In *Fig. 46* (*c*) and (*d*) a boat is shown sailing on a reach. We will assume that in (*c*) the sail is full and drawing hard. But it may be that by starting the mainsheet to the angle shown in (*d*) it can still be full and drawing. But as a result of easing the sheet the resultant force of the

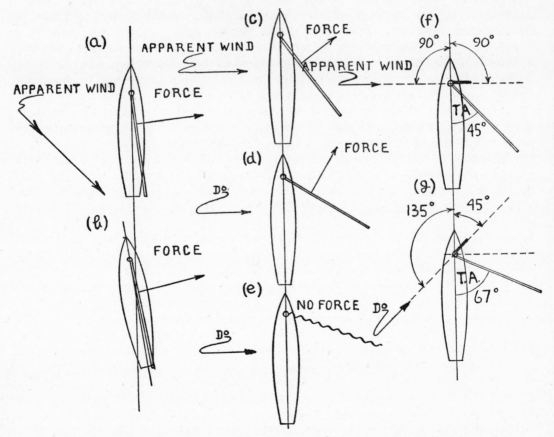

Figure 46.—The elements of sail trimming—beating, close reaching, and broad reaching.

wind developed by the sails, which will be at much the same angle to the boom in either case, swings more nearly in line with the fore and aft line of the boat. This will be obvious from a comparison of the angles of the two arrows labelled " Drive." More of the wind's force becomes available for driving the boat, and less of it causes heel and leeway.

If however the mainsheet is started farther the luff of the mainsail will begin to lift; if farther the whole mainsail will do so and there will be no heel, no leeway and no drive (e).

Here then we have the essence of all sail trimming, whether mainsail or headsails, when close reaching. But we have, to some extent, over-simplified the problem. Most boats will not be Una rigged like the one shown and as soon as we have two or more sails operating in combination one will affect another. Again, in altering the trim of the mainsail from (c) to (d) we have not only changed the angle of the boom to the line of motion but also its angle to the wind. The wind acts on the sail at a different angle of incidence and this will alter the amount of the driving force as well as its direction. It might be conceivable that though in (c) the direction of the driving force is more effective than in (d) its amount might be less. But such effects as these are difficult to analyse in practice; these are refinements in trim which long experience with a boat will reveal. But items (i) and (ii) above provide the first, close approximation to the right trim. A further consideration is the influence of the sail trim on the boat's steering. Some boats carrying heavy weather helm may be more profitably sailed with the staysail harder than is ideal. The staysail then gives less useful drive but the weather helm, and hence the resistance of the hull, may be reduced. But the good modern boat is well balanced and allows the most effective trimming of the sails to be adopted.

To summarise, when the wind is anywhere from a little more than four points off the bow to a little less than square on the beam, the principle of trimming a headsail, whether it is a staysail, jib or Genoa, is to ease the sheet until some part of the sail lifts. This part should be the luff of the sail and the quiver should extend from head to tack. Then the sheet should be hardened until, and only until, the shivering has stopped and the canvas is asleep. The way in which canvas shivers will reveal whether the sheet lead is right for the point of sailing.

Broad Reaching.—When sailing with the wind on or abaft the beam, the angle between the sail and the centre line of the boat, labelled T.A. or trim angle in *Fig. 46* (*f*) and (*g*) should be a half of the angle of the apparent wind from the bow. Another way of judging the angle is to say that the angle of the sail should be one-half of that between the burgee or other wind indicator and the stern. This may be easier to visualise and produces the same result. The two examples shown in *Fig. 46* should clarify this matter.

In judging the trim angle we must take a line about midway between the boom and the head of the sail. Thus the boom will be at a rather smaller angle to the centreline than that shown, and near the headboard it will be greater owing to the undesirable but inevitable twist in the sail; but the mean angle of the sail will be approximately that shown.

It may seem that in judging the trim of a sail by this method of angles we are adopting an apparently different principle from that used when trimming on a beat or close reach. In fact the principle is similar in all cases.

We have seen that when beating headsails should be very flat. This is arranged partly by the sailmaker, partly by the right arrangement of the sheet leads on the deck. For windward work all headsails except the Genoa will need their sheets led inside the shrouds. The Genoa sheet will lead outside all shrouds, and be hardened in until the sheet, or foot of the sail, bears on the shroud.

When broad reaching a more flowing sail is needed. A specially cut sail may be used. More usually, however, the same sail, but with the sheet leads moved aft, thus reducing the tension in the leech. Whether the right position has been found will be judged, as we have seen, by the lifting of the sail. And the sheet will be started as far as possible without allowing the sail to lift.

Trysails.—One of the original objects of a trysail was to allow the very long and heavy mainboom to be secured in its crutch when in a bad seaway. The shorter, lighter booms of to-day make this a less urgent necessity; though the trysail still has its vital rôle should the boom be damaged. Modern, small mainsails, which when close reefed are very small indeed, may also be kept set under conditions when the older fashion big mainsail and heavy gaff would have had to be replaced by the trysail. The trysail remains, however, an essential sail in a well found yacht.

Trysails are sometimes made of flax, and in the deep water cruiser this is best; but cotton is now generally chosen for the average yacht. The cloths are usually run parallel with the leech, this giving greater strength at the expense of aerodynamic properties, which are the lesser important in such a sail. Various other methods of cutting this sail have been tried, but this is the most usual. Trysails are generally roped on all sides for strength, though the poorly setting sail which may result from this discourages the roping of the leech and the acceptance of less strength.

Trysails may be cut like a jib, with the foot rising from the tack, or more generally in the older fashion were cut with a downward slope to the foot, the tack being above the clew. This is suitable when the trysail is sheeted to the quarters, but even with this arrangement a good lead for the sheet is more easily obtained when the foot of the sail is a rising line; and this cut of sail may alternatively be sheeted on to the mainboom.

This is now a common practice. The clew pendant of the trysail is secured to the boom, and the sail is sheeted with the mainsheet. So long as the boom is light, easily handled, and undamaged this makes the sheeting of the trysail easier, and manoeuvring is possible with fewer hands. When a trysail is sheeted to the quarter, double sheets with the necessary purchases are rigged on either side of the boom, which is stowed in its crutch. When tacking with a double-sheeted trysail the danger of blocks and sheets flaying in the air is reduced if the hitherto leeward sheet, which was the active one prior to tacking, is not touched until the sail itself has gone over on to the other tack. As it does so any slack in the hitherto idle sheet is taken up; then, when the sail is settled, the old leeward sheet, which is now to weather, is gently eased, and the weight simultaneously taken in the other sheet.

Trysails may have hanks on the luff and be set on the mainsail track. This necessitates a magazine track on the lower part of the mast long enough to accommodate the lowered trysail (Plate 69), and with a switch point or slide connecting the trysail track with the mainsail track. The switch point has to be high enough to allow the mainsail to be stowed below it, and in large craft this puts it out of comfortable reach.

The older system of lacing the trysail to the mast should be kept in reserve in case of mechanical trouble with the track and switch point. Separate lanyards at each grommet or eyelet in the sail are used for lacing. The middle of the lanyard is secured to its grommet, and in one end an eyesplice is worked, there being a toggle in the other for engagement with it. Parrel beads on the lanyard prevent fouling on the mast.

17

SOME MODERN SAIL PLANS

THE sail plans reproduced in this chapter have been selected from the monthly Design Supplements of the *Yachting World*, by kind permission of the Editor. The selection affords practical examples of rigs of different types and sizes. I have added notes on each to emphasize its characteristics, which I hope may assist the reader in arriving at his own conclusions.

They are as follows:—

A Gunter Lug Rig
A Simple Sloop Rig
An Efficient Gaff Rig
Sloop Rig with Unusual Features
For World Cruising
An Older Conception of the Cutter Rig
Masthead Rig: Small Mainsail, Large Fore-triangle
A Moderate Masthead Rig
International Cruiser/Racer
Sloop: Large Mainsail, Small Fore-triangle
Sloop Rig for Light Displacement Hull
A Masthead Ketch

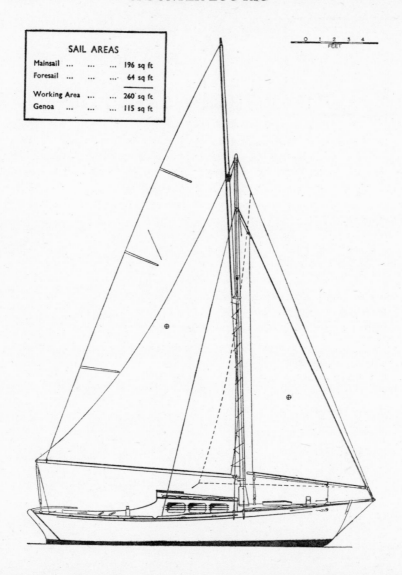

SAIL AREAS			
Mainsail	...	...	...	196 sq ft
Foresail	...	...	...	64 sq ft
Working Area	...	...	260 sq ft
Genoa	...	...	...	115 sq ft

For boats as small as this 21-ft. centreboarder by Frederick Parker, M.I.N.A., the gunter lug, which was once the common rig of all small craft, still retains features which may make its choice advantageous. When a mast is in a tabernacle and has to be lowered frequently, the reduction in its length made possible by the rig is a valuable feature. The elimination of the track and slides and the simpler staying of the mast makes the rig cheaper than the Bermudian, and it is more amenable to rough handling.

It is important in the gunter rig to ensure a good fit on the mast at the gaff jaws, and to reeve the mainsail luff lacing so that there is no likelihood of it jamming when the halyard is let go. Rather than the spiral lacing shown the line should be rove so that it enters and leaves each eyelet round the same side of the mast.

The gunter rig may have a single halyard, and the point of attachment on the gaff should not be less than about four-ninths of its length from the heel.

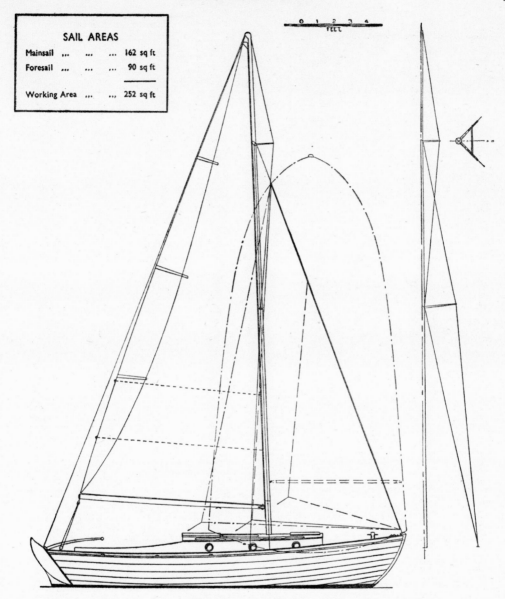

SAIL AREAS			
Mainsail	...	...	...	162 sq ft
Foresail	...	...	...	90 sq ft
Working Area	...	...	252 sq ft

    This rig for a 22-ft. over-all centreboarder by Baron van Hoevell is selected as an example of a modern, simple sloop rig of high efficiency but without any extreme features. The luff-foot ratio of the mainsail is 2·5 : 1, the ratio of mainsail area to jib is moderate, and likewise the height of the foretriangle. The sail plan shows a Genoa of 120 sq. ft. and a small jib.
    It will be seen that though the boat has a transom stern, a standing backstay has been arranged without resorting to a bumpkin. No runners are shown, and though the long jumper struts angled well forward will allow the weight in the headsail luff to be carried by the standing backstay without any considerable loss of efficiency, a slight improvement in performance might be expected using runners; though at the sacrifice of the exceptionally easy handling qualities of the rig as drawn.

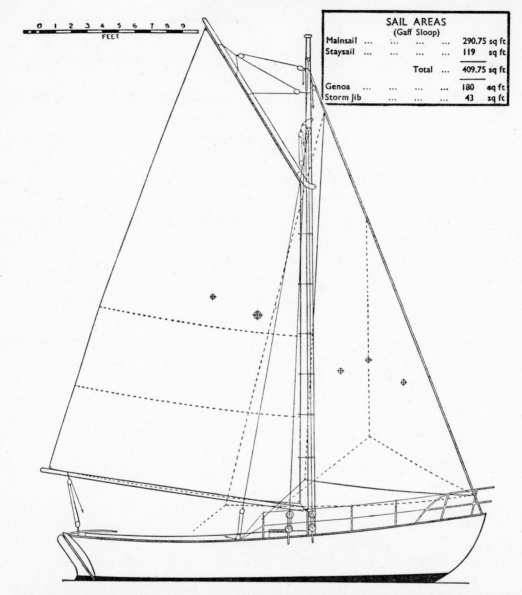

SAIL AREAS					
(Gaff Sloop)					
Mainsail	...	...	...	...	290.75 sq ft
Staysail	...	...	...	...	119 sq ft
			Total	...	409.75 sq ft
Genoa	...	...	...	...	180 sq ft
Storm Jib	...	...	...	...	43 sq ft

In this dayboat of 26 ft. 6 in. over-all, Morgan Giles has drawn a refined version of the working Falmouth Quay Punt. An efficient gaff rig with a long luff to the mainsail and a short gaff allows 410 sq. ft. of working sail to be set on a 30-ft. mast, whereas the same boat rigged as a Bermudian sloop carries 320 sq. ft. on a 37-ft. mast. The gaff rig is cheaper in first cost and maintenance, and in this case shows to advantage, allowing enough sail area to drive a fairly heavy hull fast in light and moderate winds without excessive height of rig.

The disadvantages of the rig are the two halyards, the lack of a standing backstay, and hence a reliance on the runners, and the big area of mainsail—about 25 per cent greater than the Bermudian mainsail designed for this boat—which combine to make the gaff rigged edition a harder boat to handle.

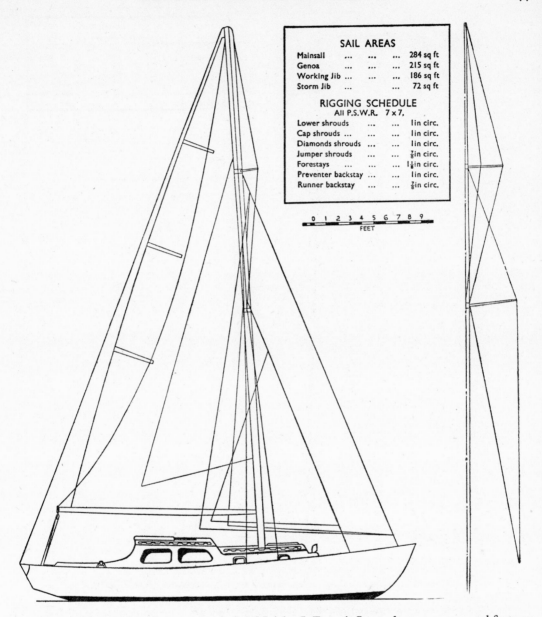

SAIL AREAS

Mainsail	... ...	...	284 sq ft
Genoa	...	...	215 sq ft
Working Jib	... ...	...	186 sq ft
Storm Jib	...	...	72 sq ft

RIGGING SCHEDULE
All P.S.W.R. 7 x 7.

Lower shrouds	...	...	1in circ.
Cap shrouds	...	...	1in circ.
Diamonds shrouds	...	...	1in circ.
Jumper shrouds	...	...	$\frac{7}{8}$in circ.
Forestays	...	...	$1\frac{1}{8}$in circ.
Preventer backstay	...	1in circ.
Runner backstay	...	...	$\frac{7}{8}$in circ.

0 1 2 3 4 5 6 7 8 9
FEET

The sloop rig of this 8-tonner (25 ft. L.W.L.) by J. Francis Jones shows two unusual features —the lower or inner forestay and a mast designed to stand without runners except when the biggest Genoa is set.

The lower forestay, apart from the desirable support which it gives to the mast between the upper spreader and the deck, allows the storm jib to be set on it. This obviates one fault of the normal sloop, in which the storm headsail has to be set on a stay near the stemhead, which may under certain conditions be too far forward. Another method of overcoming this difficulty is to set the storm staysail flying, an eyebolt being provided on the foredeck and a halyard at the lower spreaders.

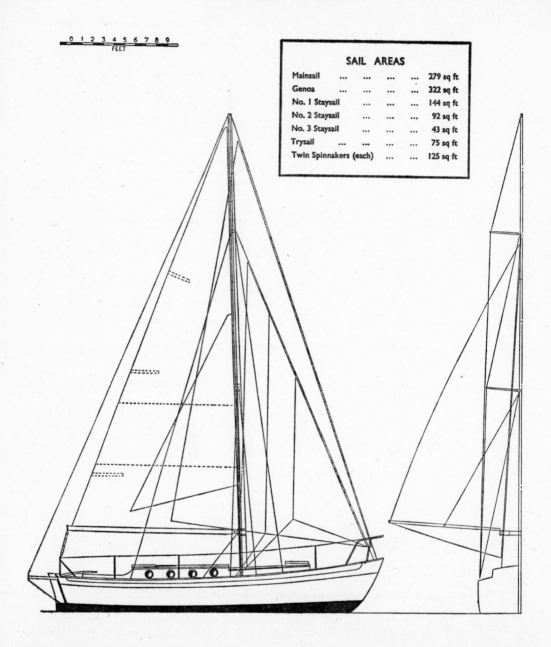

SAIL AREAS				
Mainsail	...	...	...	279 sq ft
Genoa	...	...	...	322 sq ft
No. 1 Staysail	...	...	...	144 sq ft
No. 2 Staysail	...	...	...	92 sq ft
No. 3 Staysail	...	...	...	43 sq ft
Trysail	...	...	...	75 sq ft
Twin Spinnakers (each)	...	...		125 sq ft

This rig of *Wanderer III*, designed by Laurent Giles, is Eric Hiscock's choice for a world cruise, and so deserves careful study. The Bermudian rig was chosen because it was considered easier to roll and unroll a reef than to hand a topsail, and the preference given to a sloop was due to the difficulty of avoiding narrow and inefficient headsails in a cutter with a snubbed bow and no bowsprit. The masthead sloop rig with a lower forestay gives almost the same security as a cutter, and allows a masthead stay for light canvas with a lower forestay for working canvas.

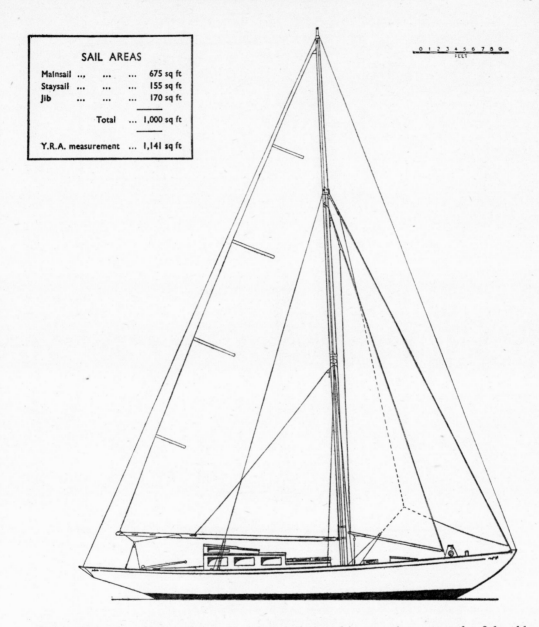

SAIL AREAS			
Mainsail ..., ...	675 sq ft
Staysail	155 sq ft
Jib	170 sq ft
Total ...	1,000 sq ft
Y.R.A. measurement ...	1,141 sq ft

This sail plan by Alfred Milne & Co., though designed in 1949, is an example of the older conception of the cutter rig. This is seen in the low aspect ratio mainsail of large area—two-thirds of the total—and the two narrow headsails which leave the mast from almost the same point. It will also be seen that a topmast forestay is fitted in lieu of jumper stays. No jib topsail is shown, and this rig is essentially that of the old three headsail cutter.

The low topping lift, rove through blocks and the lower spreader, will be seen, and the mainsheet upper block riding on boom slings; also the purchase in the runner giving a power which will enable the runner to be set up without a winch.

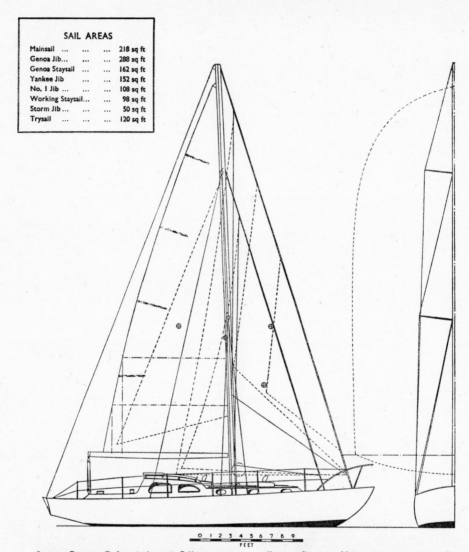

SAIL AREAS		
Mainsail	218 sq ft
Genoa Jib...	288 sq ft
Genoa Staysail	162 sq ft
Yankee Jib	152 sq ft
No. I Jib	108 sq ft
Working Staysail... ...	98 sq ft
Storm Jib	50 sq ft
Trysail	120 sq ft

0 1 2 3 4 5 6 7 8 9
FEET

STANDING RIGGING. Preformed wire rope, all 1in circ. except preventer (⅞in circ.), swaged fittings. Rigging screws closed barrel type, forged aluminium bronze, with good radii at changes of section. Shroud, forestay and foretopmast stay screws proof tested at 1,200lb, preventer backstay screws to 1,000lb.

RUNNING RIGGING. Main and staysail halyards ½in circ. flexible S.W.R. Jib halyard ⅝in. Spinnaker halyard 1¼in hemp with ¼in wire in way of block, double-ended with snap-shackle each end. Mainsheet 1½in nylon. All headsail sheets single-part 1¼in nylon with snap-shackles.

This is an example of the masthead cutter rig by J. A. Knowler, in a 24-ft. waterline Class III ocean racer, at which size the sloop is more usually chosen, and it shows an advanced interpretation of the small mainsail and large fore-triangle principle. The result is a mainsail of only 218 sq. ft. (it is of interest to compare this with the Quay Punt's mainsail) and a fore-triangle in which may be set a masthead Genoa of 288 sq. ft. or combinations of the six headsails which comprise the wardrobe.

It is thus a complicated rig, but one offering a very well stayed mast, an easily handled mainsail, and except for the masthead Genoa, small sails forward of the mast. It is the strongest and most flexible rig which has been devised.

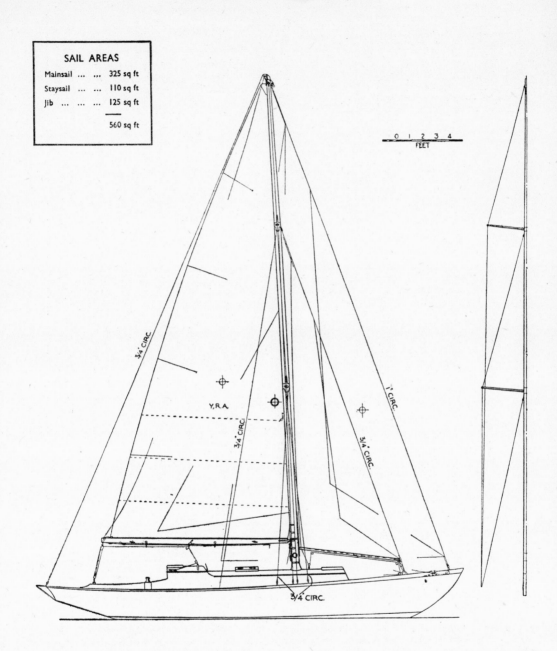

SAIL AREAS

Mainsail	...	...	325 sq ft
Staysail	...	...	110 sq ft
Jib	...	...	125 sq ft
			560 sq ft

Mokoia by Arthur Robb is another example of the masthead cutter of less extreme type, and in a larger boat (30 ft. L.W.L.). The mainsail is proportionately more of the total sail area. The wardrobe of headsails consists of a masthead Genoa, two smaller jibs, a staysail set on a club and therefore self-trimming, and a storm staysail. *Mokoia* was one of the three Class III ocean racers which took part in the Transatlantic Race of 1950.

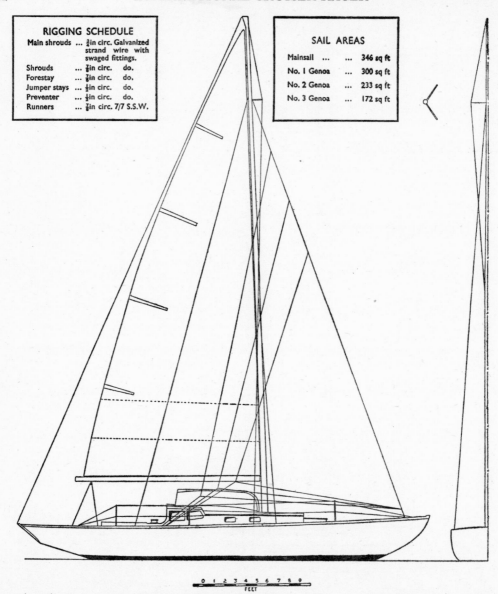

RIGGING SCHEDULE

Main shrouds ... ¾in circ. Galvanized
                strand wire with
                swaged fittings.
Shrouds   ... ⅞in circ. do.
Forestay   ... ⅞in circ. do.
Jumper stays ... ⅜in circ. do.
Preventer   ... ⅜in circ. do.
Runners   ... ⅞in circ. 7/7 S.S.W.

SAIL AREAS

Mainsail	...	346 sq ft
No. 1 Genoa	...	300 sq ft
No. 2 Genoa	...	233 sq ft
No. 3 Genoa	...	172 sq ft

Sonda's sail plan shows the interpretation of the rig clauses of the International Cruiser-Racer Rule by James McGruer, who played the leading part in producing the rule. The result is a sloop rig without any extreme features, either in the mainsail's aspect ratio or in the ratio of mainsail to fore-triangle.

The cut of the three headsails should be noticed. With each reduction in sail area the luff of the Genoa is reduced considerably in length, and the angle at the peak increased. Thus, in stronger winds, the leech of the headsail is well clear of the luff of the mainsail, reducing the backwinding of the mainsail which may become severe under such conditions, whilst the avoidance of narrowness at the top of the headsail allows a better setting sail.

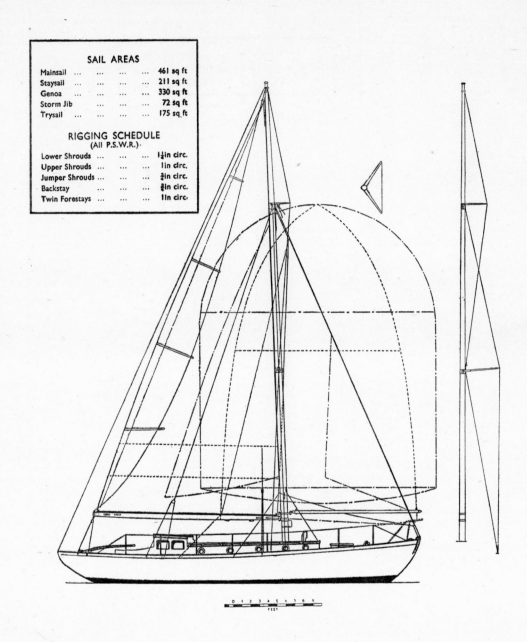

SAIL AREAS

Mainsail	...	...	...	461 sq ft
Staysail	...	...	...	211 sq ft
Genoa	...	...	...	330 sq ft
Storm Jib	...	...	...	72 sq ft
Trysail	...	...	...	175 sq ft

RIGGING SCHEDULE
(All P.S.W.R.)·

Lower Shrouds	...	...	...	1¼in circ.
Upper Shrouds	...	...	...	1in circ.
Jumper Shrouds	...	...	...	¾in circ.
Backstay	...	...	...	¾in circ.
Twin Forestays	...	...	...	1in circ.

The rig of *Saluki* is that of a very moderate cruising sloop with a large mainsail and small fore-triangle. In such a rig the mainsail lives up to its name, and the rôle of the headsails is reduced in importance. The staying of the mast is very simple for the size of boat, and the jumper struts and stays serve as the upper spreaders and topmast shrouds.

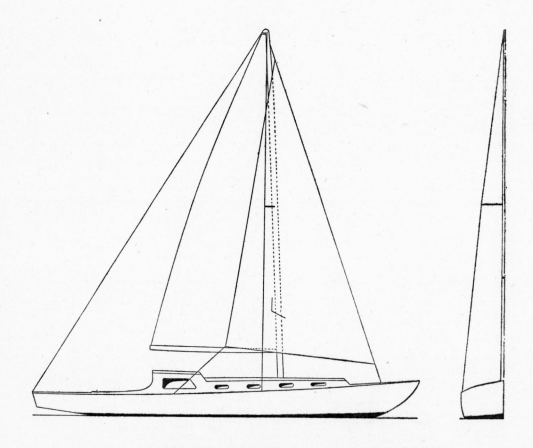

SAIL AREAS			
Mainsail ...	...	...	... 293 sq ft
Jib	...	...	... 323 sq ft

This is the masthead sloop rig for very light displacement hull of 35 ft. on the waterline, designed by Uffa Fox. It represents the ultimate simplicity in rig, and is designed primarily for sailing with the wind free. The small mainsail, and Genoa of about 10 per cent greater area, and the masthead rig, combine to reduce the performance to windward.

The staying of the mast had in practice to be elaborated.

SAIL AREAS				
Mainsail	...	...	...	450 sq ft
Mizzen	...	...	...	115 sq ft
Staysail	...	...	...	190 sq ft
Yankee	...	...	...	294 sq ft
Total	...	...	...	1,049 sq ft

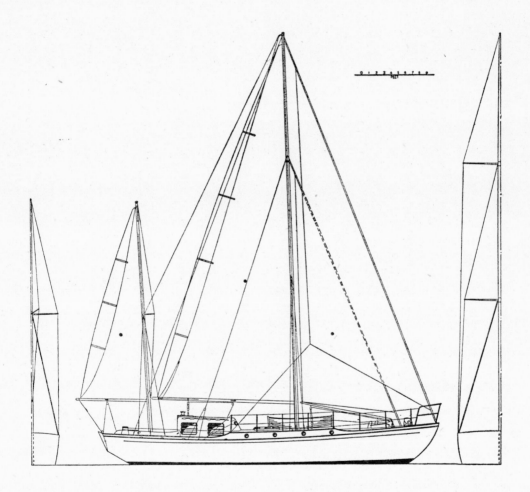

In this ketch of 47 ft. over all by Thornycroft the masthead rig has been adopted, with a large fore-triangle, and a mainmast supported by twin standing backstays to the quarters. The club on the foot of the staysail allows this sail to be self-trimming, but being pivoted a few inches abaft the tack of the sail, the club swings with a smaller radius than the foot of the sail, which obviates the objectionable flattening of the foot of the sail.

Appendix I

C.C.A. RULE. SAIL MEASUREMENT

RIG AND SAIL MEASUREMENTS, 1954

General.—For most of the measurements described in this section, detailed procedures are given whereby they may be determined on a fair basis under ordinary circumstances. However, if these procedures are found not to cover completely in individual cases, the measurer will decide how best to get a reliable figure for the measurement in question. For instance, where masts enter through cabin trunk tops, the theoretical intersection of the centreline of the main deck with the masts can be determined by certification from the designer if it cannot be ascertained directly by inspection and auxiliary measurements.

Base S.A.—**Base Sail Area.**—

$$\sqrt{\text{Base S.A.}} = 4.3 \sqrt[3]{\text{Base Disp.}}$$

R.S.A.—**Rated Sail Area.**—The total of the Rated Areas (R.A.) included for the Rig in question, in accordance with the following:—

(*a*) *Cat Rig*—R.S.A. = Mainsail R.A.

(*b*) *Sloop or Cutter*—R.S.A. = Mainsail R.A. + Fore Triangle R.A.

(*c*) *Yawl or Ketch*—R.S.A. = Mainsail R.A. + Fore Triangle R.A. + Mizzen R.A.

(*d*) *Schooner (2-masted)*—

$$\text{R.S.A.} = \left(\frac{\text{Mainsail R.A.} \times \text{Mainsail R.A.}}{\text{Mainsail R.A.} + \text{M.A. Bet. Masts}} \right)$$
$$+ \text{ Fore Triangle R.A.} + \text{R.A. Bet. Masts}$$

(*e*) *Other Rigs.*—A study of details for measurement of rigs specifically covered above should point the way to appropriate measurement of other rigs.

"S"—**Sail Area Correction**—(as used in the formula) is determined as follows:—

(*a*) If $\sqrt{\text{R.S.A.}}$ exceeds $\sqrt{\text{Base S.A.}}$, multiply the excess by 1.15 to get "S" and insert as a plus quantity.

(*b*) If $\sqrt{\text{R.S.A.}}$ is less than $\sqrt{\text{Base S.A.}}$, "S" equals the difference, and is a minus quantity.

Mainsail R.A.—**Mainsail Rated Area.**—

(*a*) *Jib-headed Mainsail R.A.* = .5 B × P + .25 B(P − 2B)
(a-1) If P does not exceed 2B, R.A. = .5 B × P

(*b*) *Gaff Main R.A.* = .4 [(B × H) + (G $\sqrt{B^2 + H^2}$)]
(b-1) If topsail is used, 75 per cent of topsail M.A. must be added to Mainsail R.A.
(b-2) *Topsail Measured Area*—shall be the area calculated from the measurement of the three sides by taking the height from the upper point of the mainsail hoist to the highest point to which the topsail may be set, including sprit, if any; the length of the gaff (G) to which it is sheeted, plus extension of club, if any; and the length of the leach measured from the sail when dry and stretched hard taut.

Fore Triangle R.A.—**Fore Triangle Rated Area**—may be calculated as selected at the time of measurement, either for *Racing Canvas* (Rac), or for *Cruising Canvas* (Cru):

(a) Fore Triangle R.A. (*Rac*) $= .6\,B_2 \times P_2 + .25\,B_2(P_2 - 2B_2)$
   (a-1) if P_2 does not exceed 2 B_2, Fore Triangle R.A. (*Rac*) $= .6\,B_2 \times P_2$

(b) Fore Triangle R.A. (*Cru*) $= .5\,B_2 \times P_2$

Mizzen R.A.—**Mizzen** *RATED* **Area** (yawls and ketches):—

(a) If Mizzen Measured Area is less than or equals, 10 per cent of the sum of Main R.A. + Fore Triangle R.A., then: Mizzen R.A. $= .5$ Mizzen M.A.

(b) If Mizzen Measured Area exceeds 10 per cent of the sum of Main R.A. + Fore Triangle R.A., but does not exceed 50 per cent of this sum, then: Mizzen R.A. $= .05$ (Main R.A. + Fore Triangle R.A.) $+ .25$ [(Mizzen M.A. $- .1$ (Main R.A. + Fore Triangle R.A.)]

(c) If Mizzen Measured Area exceeds 50 per cent of Main R.A. + Fore Triangle R.A., yacht should be measured as a schooner.

Mizzen M.A.—**Mizzen** *MEASURED* **Area** (yawls and ketches)—is determined similarly to Mainsail R.A. The same letters should be used with the suffix "miz" in listing the dimensions and calculating the areas.

R.A. Between the Masts—*RATED* **Area Between the Masts**—(2-masted Schooners) is dependent on type and number of sails used between the masts, as follows:—

(a) Staysail rigged schooners: R.A. between the masts = M.A. between the masts.

(b) Gaff foresail or jib-headed foresail schooners, either with the maximum of two main topmast staysails: R.A. between the masts = .75 M.A. between the masts.
   (b-1) Gaff foresail or jib-headed foresail schooners wishing to have the same freedom regarding sails set between the masts as permitted in the case of staysail rigged schooners, may do so by being rated for 100 per cent of the area between the masts.

(c) Gaff foresail or jib-headed foresails where no other sails are used between the masts: R.A. between the masts = R.A. of foresail taken as for a gaff or jib-headed mainsail.

M.A. Between the Masts—*MEASURED* **Area Between the Masts** (2-masted Schooners):—

(a) For staysail rigged schooners, and gaff foresail or jib-headed foresail schooners which use other sails between the masts: M.A. between the masts $= .5\,B_1\,(P_1 + P_3)$.

(b) Gaff foresail or jib-headed foresail schooners with no other sails between the masts: M.A. between the masts = twice R.A. of foresail taken as for a gaff or jib-headed mainsail.

B—**Determination of B.**—B is the measured length of the main boom, taken from the after side of mast or fair extension of track if used, to extreme aftermost position to which the sail can be extended. If this latter point is inside of boom end, it must be located by inner edge of 1-inch black band around boom, together with suitable stopper to prevent sail being extended beyond measurement point.

(a) If in yawls and ketches the distance from the forward side of the mizzen mast to the after point of the B measurement exceeds .20B, this excess multiplied by Pmiz shall be added to the total measured sail area.

(b) For staysail ketch, B = distance between masts.

P—**Determination of P.**—Measured hoist of jib-headed mainsail, taken along afterside of mainmast between the top of boom, produced fairly, or boom track if used, produced fairly, and the top of the highest sheave used for the main halyard; or to the underside of 1-inch black band, provided either a fixed stopper or accurate halyard marking will indicate exactly when highest part of sail reaches underside of band.

   (*a*)   If sliding gooseneck is used, measurement is to be made with boom at extreme bottom of travel.   If this point is determined by a removable stopper, upper edge of 1-inch black band around mast must locate measurement point below which point top of boom (or track) may not be carried when mainsail is set.

   (*b*)   The low point used in determination of P may not be taken higher than .05 P + 2.25 feet above main deck.

   (*c*)   If boom gooseneck is above tack of sail, maximum distance from gooseneck to tack must be added to P dimension as otherwise measured.

   (*d*)   If rake of mast exceeds 15 per cent, P shall be taken as the *vertical* height.

H—**Determination of H.**—Measured Hoist for Gaff Mainsail is a perpendicular measured along the afterside of the mast from the lower edge of 1-inch black band around the mast, above which mark the upper inner edge of the throat cringle of the mainsail shall not be hoisted, to the upper side of the boom or black band, the location of which is covered by regulations applying to P.

G—**Determination of G.**—Length of main gaff is measured when gaff is lying on top of boom, and is the distance from afterside of mast to outboard point of gaff, its determination being similar to that of outboard end of main boom.

B₂—**Determination of B₂.**—Base used in calculating the Fore Triangle—B₂ is taken as whichever of the following is greatest:

   (*a*)   *J—Actual Fore Triangle Base*, which is the distance from the foreside of the mast at the deck to the centreline of the foremost stay on which headsails are set (the centreline of the luff if the foremost headsail is set flying), extended if necessary, to intersect the top of the bowsprit, or if no bowsprit, the top of the rail, including cap if used, and extended if necessary, or to the centreline of the deck, if same is above the rail or rail cap.

   (*b*)   *Spinnaker Pole Length*: Spinnaker pole is measured when set horizontal on the mast and at right-angles to the centreline of the yacht, measurement being from the centerline to the extreme outboard end of the pole, including all fixed fittings.

   (*c*)   *A Percentage of Spinnaker Measured Width*: As determined by measurement of spinnaker width in conjunction with the appropriate of the following formulae:—
        (c-1) *Racing Canvas*: Maximum spinnaker width ÷ 1.8
        (c-2) *Cruising Canvas*: Maximum spinnaker width ÷ 1.3

P₂—**Determination of P₂.**—*Height used in calculating the Fore Triangle R.A.* is taken as whichever of the following is greater:—

   (*a*)   *Actual Fore Triangle Height*, measured along the fore side of the mast from the intersection of the main deck centreline (produced if necessary), to whichever is highest of the following:—

        (a-1) The intersection of the centreline of the highest stay used for headsails, with the fair line of the foreside of the mast or topmast (produced if necessary).

(a-2) The centre of the highest eyebolt or eye used for headsail or spinnaker halyard block. A spinnaker halyard block may be set forward enough to produce a clear lead, without measurement penalty.

(a-3) To intersection of the foreside of the mast or topmast (produced if necessary) with the highest strop used for headsail or spinnaker halyard.

(b)   *Length Determined by Spinnaker Dimensions,* using a value of $P_2 = \sqrt{\left(\dfrac{l}{.95}\right)^2 - B_2{}^2}$ where l is length of luff or leach whichever is greater.

Bmiz—**Determination of Bmiz.**—Base used in calculating Mizzen M.A. (yawls and ketches) is determined in a manner similar to that used in determining B, except that Bmiz may not be taken as less than a value which has the same ratio to Pmiz as B has to P.

Pmiz—**Determination of Pmiz.**—Height used in calculating Mizzen M.A. (yawls and ketches) is determined in a manner similar to that used in determining P except that the upper point of measurement for the mizzen cannot be taken below the measured height of the attachment of the mizzen staysail halyard block or top of sheave, which may be hung sufficiently forward of the mast to provide a clear lead for the halyard without requiring the height measurement to be obtained by extending a line through the point of support, providing the mizzen staysail halyard block is no further from the mast than necessary for clearance. Note that the lower point of Pmiz may not be taken higher than .05 Pmiz + 3.25 above the main deck.

Hmiz—**Determination of Hmiz.**—Hoist of gaff mizzen determined in a manner similar to that used in determining H. The upper limit may not be taken as less than 80 per cent from the lower limit to the mizzen staysail halyard block.

Gmiz—**Determination of Gmiz.**—Length of mizzen gaff is determined in a manner similar to that used in determining G.

B_1—**Determination of B_1** (2-masted schooners)—This is the distance measured at the deck from the foreside of the mainmast to the afterside of the foremast (or fair extension of track if used).

> (Note that if there is any overlap of the foresail or lower main staysail beyond the fore side of the main mast, this overlap must be added to the distance between the masts in determining B_1.)

P_1—**Determination of P_1** (2-masted schooners)—This is a perpendicular measured along the afterside of the foremast from the higher of the following points: the top of the highest sheave in the mast, or the highest juncture of the mast with the eyebolt (center of eye) or pennant of a halyard block, used for sails aft of the mast; to the upper side of the boom or track, when resting against the lower part of the gooseneck or when resting on the saddle, or to a black band if no boom is carried, such lower points to be no higher above the deck than the corresponding point on the mainmast. Exception: Peak Halyard Blocks are to be disregarded in taking this measurement.

P_3—**Determination of P_3** (2-masted schooners)—This is a perpendicular measured along the foreside of the mainmast from the higher of the following points: the top of the highest sheave in the mast, or the highest juncture of the mast with the eyebolt (center of eye) or pennant of a halyard block, used for sails forward of the mast; to the extension of the upper side of the boom or track of the foresail, or the lower main staysail when resting parallel to the deck against the lower part of the gooseneck, or when resting on the saddle; or to a point the same height above the deck as the tack of the foresail or lower main staysail if no boom is carried.

N

Mainsail Headboard and Batten Limits and Measurement.—

(a) *Headboards:* In jib-headed mainsails shall be limited to 3 per cent of B. Any excess shall be added to B in computing mainsail rated area. (This does not apply to sails in use prior to 1st January, 1950.)

(b) *Battens:* The number of battens in any single sail shall be limited to four, except in the case of mainsails where B exceeds 40 feet, in which case five battens may be used. Upper and lower battens shall not exceed 10 per cent of B, + 1 foot, and intermediate battens 12 per cent of B, + 1 foot. In the event of any excess, the total shall be added to B in computing mainsail rated area.

Measurement and Rating of Unusual Mainsails.—

(a) *Mainsail Rated Area of Staysail Ketch* = .5B (P + Pmiz) + .25B (P − 2B) using distance between masts for B.

(b) *Rates Area of Quadrilateral Mainsail* (other than gaff sail) or other unusual mainsail, is to be taken as the actual area plus its aspect ratio tax, if P exceeds 2B.

(c) *Mainsails Without Booms:* Where these are used, the B measurements is the maximum measurement of the sail when new, and the dimension should be marked and initialled on the sail by the measurer.

(d) *Gaff Mainsails:* If gaff is less than .6B or peaks higher than 70 degrees above horizontal, Mainsail R.A. will be figured at 100 per cent + aspect ratio tax if H + G exceeds 2B.

(e) *Main Topmast Backstay Sails* (*Mules*) as used on jib-headed ketches or yawls, must have 70 per cent of their area as determined by the maximum limits of halyard, tack, and sheeting points added to the otherwise determined mainsail rated area, to arrive at final mainsail rated area to be used for these rigs. The Mule will be classified as a Main Topsail, so that one conventional mizzen staysail can be carried in addition.

Spinnaker Measurements and Limitations.—All measurements are to be taken with such tension in the sail as will produce, as nearly as possible, an approximation of the size when set running before a moderate breeze. Head of sails measured under this Rule to be signed and marked by the measurer with the maximum length of the luff or the leach (whichever is greater) and with the maximum width that can be found in the sail, measuring between points on the luff and leach equidistant from the head. These marked dimensions can be used as long as the sail is used without alteration. Headboard shall not be longer than one-twentieth of the length of the spinnaker pole. No footyard or other contrivance for extending the sail to other than a triangular shape shall be used.

(NOTE: Sails certified under the 1940 C.C.A. Rule can be used on the boat for which they were certified, under the originally certified dimensions, as long as neither the sail nor the boat's fore triangle has been altered.)

(a) *Spinnaker Maximum Length:* Luff and leach may not exceed $.95 \sqrt{P_2{}^2 + B_2{}^2}$

(b) *Spinnaker Maximum Width*

(b-1) Under *Racing Canvas Rating*, spinnaker width may not exceed 180 per cent of B_2.

(b-2) Under *Cruising Canvas Rating*, spinnaker may not exceed 130 per cent of B_2.

Miscellaneous Mizzen Limitations.—(Applies to Yawl and Ketch)—The Mizzen is subject to limitations. (The headboard limitation is 5 per cent of Bmiz.) (For sails not in use prior to 1st January, 1950.) Excess mizzen batten length to be added to Bmiz.

(a) A sail set on the main permanent backstay of a single masted yacht shall be classified as a mizzen and measured for its actual area, but final rated area to be taken at 50 per cent of what it would be for a conventional mizzen.

(NOTE that no mizzen staysail can be carried with this rig.)

Measurement and Rating of Sails Between the Masts of Schooners.—

(a) *Foresails* are subject to restrictions similar to those specifically listed for Mainsails, and overlapping foresails are subject to foot measurement.

(b) *Staysail Rigged Schooners* (and gaff or jib-headed foresail schooners accepting 100 per cent charge for area between the masts) are subject to no restriction on size and number of sails between the masts other than the measurement of overlap of the largest lower main staysail that is used, if it overlaps the fore side of the mainmast.

(c) *With Gaff Foresail or Jib-Headed Foresail* (accepting 75 per cent charge for area between masts) two main topmast staysails may be carried, one of which must be a *bona fide* Fisherman staysail, and the other of which must be materially larger and suitable for downwind work. When the smaller sail is in use, the *regular foresail must be set at all times*, but the foresail may or may not be set when the larger staysail is being used. With the exception of boats rated for a fore topsail, which then may be carried, no other sails may be used in the space between the masts.

(d) *With Gaff Foresail or Jib-Headed Foresail* (where no other sails are used between the masts) the foresail as declared at time of measurement is the only sail that may be carried between the masts.

SAIL, SAIL TRIMMING AND RIG LIMITATIONS

General.—There are certain conflicts between the N.A.Y.R.U. and the C.C. of A. Rules governing Sail Trimming and rig limitations. Where these conflicts exist, the C.C. of A. Measurement Rule will govern in races conducted under this rule.

Trimming to Spars.—Sheets of spinnakers, headsails, mizzen staysails, and loose footed sails set between the masts of schooners, may not be trimmed to spars outside the measurement points.

Mainsails

(a) *Loose Footed Mainsails:* These are permitted only when they are the regular mainsail normally used for the boat in question. Under these conditions, when a loose footed mainsail is used, it is not permissible to carry on board a second mainsail of a different character, nor is it permissible to shift back and forth between a loose footed and a laced mainsail for various races. Rather, the selection must be made regarding mainsail type at the time the measurement certificate is issued.

(b) *Light Weight Mainsails:* These are not permitted and it is the intent of the Rule that a second mainsail may not be carried aboard as a supplement to maximum performance that would be expected from the regular mainsail, but rather, a second mainsail can only be carried as a spare for emergency replacement.

(c) *Storm Trysails:* These must be materially smaller than a normal close-reefed mainsail and of strength consistent with their intended purpose, viz., use in extremely severe weather.

Headsails.—

(a) *Headsails* may be sheeted from only one point on the sail (thus excluding quadrilateral or similar sails).

(b)   *Headsails* may be sheeted to any part of the rail or deck; or to the main boom, *when the mainsail is set*, and to spinnaker pole when pole is set on opposite side from main boom.

(c)   Under *Racing Canvas Rating* there is no limit to headsail width dimensions.

(d)   Under *Cruising Canvas Rating*, no headsails can be of a size that, considering "made" dimensions, would extend aft of the forward side of the mast to which they are set.

Spinnakers, Spinnaker Poles and Special Downwind Sails.

(a)   *Spinnaker Sheeting:* Spinnakers may be sheeted from only one point on the sail.

     (c-1) Under *Racing Canvas Rating*, spinnakers may be sheeted to any part of the rail or deck, or to the main boom, *when the mainsail is set*, but to no other spar or outrigger.

     (c-2) Under *Cruising Canvas Rating*, spinnaker sheet must be led directly to the deck or rail *inside* of all lee shrouds.

(b)   *Any bona fide headsail* otherwise permitted, may be used as a spare spinnaker without reference to spinnaker measurement requirements. Such a sail may be tacked to, or sheeted to, the spinnaker pole.

(c)   *Spinnaker Pole Limitations:* A spinnaker pole may be carried only on the windward side of the foremost mast. The inboard end may not be set higher than .18 P_2 + 2 feet above main deck.

(d)   *Spinnaker Tack:* Must be close to spinnaker pole on side opposite to main boom. (Spinnaker may not be carried without spinnaker pole.)

(e)   *Squaresail:* A yacht may carry a squaresail, square topsail, raffee, or a twin spinnaker rig, instead of a spinnaker. The actual area of such sails may not exceed the rated fore triangle area, nor may the total length of their boom or booms exceed the length of the spinnaker pole.

(f)   *Twin Spinnakers Alone:* When twin spinnakers alone are set, their total actual area must not exceed the total rated sail area of the boat. When using this sail combination, one of the two headsails or spinnakers may be trimmed to the main boom without violating rule **Headsails** (b).

Mizzen Staysail on Yawl or Ketch.—

(a)   *Sheet Leads:* Mizzen staysails may be trimmed to the rail or hull, and to the mizzen boom (whether or not the mizzen is set) but they may not be sheeted to any other spar or outrigger.

(b)   *One Mizzen Staysail Only:* Except with a staysail ketch rig with which two are allowed, only *one* mizzen staysail may be carried aboard. Type and dimensions must be selected at the time of measurement.

     (b-1) No mizzen staysail may be carried on a yawl or ketch whose mizzen is set on a permanent backstay in lieu of a conventional mizzen mast.

Sails Between the Masts in Schooners.—

(a)   *Sails Set Between the Masts* may be trimmed to any part of the rail or the deck, or to the main boom. However, when the mainsail is not set, the area of any sail set between the masts must not exceed the total measured areas of the mainsail and of the area between the masts.

(*b*)   Double clewed sails are not permitted.

(*c*)   No sail set between the masts may extend below the base points used in establishment of P_1 and P_3 measurements.

Summary of Permissible Sails.—Sails which exceed the confines which are measured and described, such as sails which could be extended above the highest points measured, or which are extended by unmeasured portable spars or outriggers, or which are tacked below the low limit of measurements, are not permitted. Following is a condensed summary of sails which are permitted:

(*a*)   *Cat Rig:* Mainsail or storm trysail and main topsail if rated for same.

(*b*)   *Sloop or Cutter:* Sails allowed a cat rig plus headsails; plus spinnakers or equivalent.

(*c*)   *Yawl or Ketch:* Sails allowed a sloop or a cutter, plus mizzen or mizzen storm trysail and mizzen topsail if rated for same, plus mizzen staysail.

(*d*)   *Two-masted Schooners:* Sails allowed a sloop or a cutter, plus sails between the masts.

(*e*)   *Miscellaneous:* A cat rig may not carry a spinnaker unless accepting this as a basis for fore triangle measurement, in which case classification and measurement would be as for a sloop or a cutter. Conversely, a schooner, yawl, or ketch which carries neither headsails nor spinnakers, may be rated without fore triangle measurement by following the normal procedures outlined in the foregoing but using zero for the fore triangle rated area.

Appendix 2

R.O.R.C. RULE. SAIL MEASUREMENT

SAIL AREA MEASUREMENT

S.A. (*Sail Area*).—Shall be the sum of all sails or areas for which a yacht has been measured.

Black Bands.—Black bands at least 1 inch in width may be used on spars. The inner edge of black band shall indicate the limit to which the sail may be stretched. In the case of the head, upper inner edge of cringle or upper edge of headboard; in the case of tack, upper side of boom; in the case of boom, the after inner edge of clew cringle.

When black bands at the head or tack of mainsail or mizzen are used, chocks or stops shall be fitted so that the sail cannot be hoisted above, or boom tacked below, the inner edge of black band.

Note.—In the case of a main or mizzen sail with a wishbone or similar boom, the upper inner edge of the tack cringle shall not be tacked below the black band. The measurement for *b* shall be taken from the black band at tack to the furthest point of outhaul on the wishbone boom when in its normal position.

Bermuda Sails—*Main and Mizzen.*—

b. Length of boom taken from the after side of mast to the outhaul, pin of slide, at its full extension aft, or to black band.

p. To be measured along the after side of the mast from the highest of the following points: The top of the highest sheave in the mast or topmast, or the highest juncture of the mast or topmast with the eyebolts (centre of eye) or pennant of a halyard block used for sails aft of the mast, or black band; to the upper side of the boom when in its lowest position, or to black band.

In yachts which carry the upper halyard block on a pennant, the upper point of measurement shall be the point at which the pennant is fastened to *the mast*.

Area for inclusion in S.A. shall be: $\dfrac{b \times p}{2}$

Bermuda Sail—*With Bent Mast.*

p. To be measured from the highest sheave, in a line parallel to the after side of the straight part of the mast, to the upper side of the boom.

b_3 is the distance from the point on the boom to which *p* is measured, to the after side of the mast.

Area for inclusion in S.A. shall be:—

$$\frac{p(b - b_3)}{2} + p \times b_3$$

Gaff Sails—*Main or Mizzen.*

b. Length of boom taken as for Bermuda sails.

g. Length of gaff when lying on the top of the boom measured from the after side of the mast to the outer end of head when fully extended.

h. To be measured along the afterside of the mast from the upper side of the boom when in its lowest position, or from black band, to the highest position to which the throat cringle of the mainsail can be hoisted, or to the lower edge of a black band above which mark the upper inner edge of the throat cringle of the mainsail shall not be hoisted.

d. Diagonal distance, from outboard end of boom to throat cringle, shall not be measured, but shall be calculated from the following formula:—

$$d = .96 \sqrt{b^2 + h^2}$$

Area for inclusion in S.A. shall be:—

$$\frac{(b \times h) + (g \times d)}{2}$$

Jib-Headed Topsails—*Main or Mizzen.*

p. To be measured as for Bermuda sails.

h. To be measured as for gaff mainsails.

l. The shortest distance measured across the topsail from the sheet cringle to the luff rope.

Area for inclusion in S.A. shall be :—$\dfrac{l(p - h)}{2}$

Yard or Jackyard Topsail.—Area shall be calculated by:—

$$\frac{\text{Luff} \times \text{Shortest Distance from Clew Cringle to Luff}}{2}$$

If this area exceeds 150 per cent of the area of the jib-headed topsail, the excess shall be added to the total sail area.

This does not apply to yachts built before December, 1939.

Schooners—*Sails between Masts.*—

(i) b_1 The distance to be measured at the deck between the foreside of the mainmast and the after-side of the foremast.

p To be measured along the afterside of the foremast from the higher of the following points: The top of the highest sheave in the mast or topmast, or the highest juncture of the mast or topmast with the eyebolt (centre of eye) or pennant of a halyard block, whether such sheave, block or pennant be used for sails forward or aft of the mast; to the upper side of the boom when in its lowest position, or to black band, or to the deck, if no boom be carried.

p_3 To be measured along the foreside of the mainmast from the highest of the following points: The top of the highest sheave in the mast or topmast or the highest juncture of the mast or topmast with the eyebolt (centre of eye) or pennant of a halyard block used for sails aft of the mast, to the upper side of the boom of the foresail, or of the lower mainstaysail, when resting parallel to the deck when in its lowest position, or when the top of the black band is in line with the upper side of boom, or to the deck if no boom be carried.

Area for inclusion in S.A. shall be:—

$$.75 \frac{p_1 + p_3}{2} \times b_1$$

(ii) The area of the sails between the main and mizzen masts in THREE-MASTED SCHOONERS shall be obtained in a similar manner from like measurements made on and between the main and mizzen masts.

Wishbone Ketches.

p. To be measured as for Bermuda sails.

b_1 To be measured as for schooners.

p_3 To be measured as for schooners, but along foreside of mizzen mast.

Area for inclusion in S.A. shall be:—

$$.85 \frac{p + p_3}{2} \times b_1$$

Fore-Triangle.—

(i) *I.* To be measured along the foreside of the mast in cutters, yawls and ketches, and of the foremast in schooners, from the deck to the higher of the following points: The top of the highest sheave in the mast or topmast used for headsails or spinnaker, or the highest juncture of the mast or topmast with the eyebolt (centre of eye) or pennant of a halyard block used for headsails or spinnaker. In no case shall the upper point of measurement be taken below the point of intersection of the line of the luff of the foremost headsail, when extended, and the mast.

J. The base J to be measured from the foreside of mast (foremast in the case of a schooner) to where the line of the luff of the foremost headsail when extended cuts the bowsprit, stem or hull.

(ii) If the following limitation of the *Spinnaker Boom, Spinnaker or Headsails* is exceeded, in addition will be made as follows to the measurement of "I" and/or "J".

Spinnaker Boom.—If the length of any spinnaker boom, measured when in position and at right angles to the centre line of the yacht, from its extreme outboard end to the centre line of yacht, exceeds the base J, the excess shall be added to J.

If the inboard end of the spinnaker boom is mounted further forward of the foreside of the mast than half the diameter of the mast measured at deck level, any excess shall be added to the length of spinnaker boom.

Spinnaker.—(i) If the length of the luff or leach of any spinnaker exceeds $.95 \sqrt{I^2 + J^2}$, the excess shall be added to the height of "I".

(ii) If the foot and/or widest part of the sail, measured between points on the luff and leach equidistant from the head, exceeds 180 per cent of the base of the fore triangle J, 55 per cent of the excess shall be added to J.

(iii) Any spinnaker in which the widest part exceeds 150 per cent J, must be symmetrical about a line joining the head with the centre of the foot, and the width of the sail at half the distance between the head and centre of a straight line joining tack and clew must not be less than 75 per cent of the width between tack and clew. If either or both of these conditions are not fulfilled the sail will be measured as a headsail and two-thirds of any excess over 150 per cent of J will be added to J.

Headsails.—If the horizontal distance between the tack of any headsail, when new, and a perpendicular dropped from the clew of the sail exceeds one and a half times the base J, two-thirds of the excess shall be added to J.

Fore triangle Penalties.—When more than one of the above penalties increasing the measurement of base J are incurred, the greatest only shall be applied.

Area of Fore triangle.—Area of fore triangle, for inclusion in S.A., shall cover all headsails and spinnakers. It shall be found after correcting values of "I" and "J" for any penalties, from the following formula:—

$$.85 \, \frac{I \times J}{2}$$

Squaresail.—If a yacht carry a squaresail, square topsail or raffee (together or separately) instead of a spinnaker, the actual area of these shall be computed; and if their area exceeds the product of "I" and "J" the excess shall be added to the total area.

Penalties.—

(i) *Mast Height:* Mast height taken from deck to highest point of sail measurement, shall not, without penalty, exceed (.96H + 4) R.A., where H = L + B + MD and R.A. = rig allowance. Half of any excess in feet shall be added to the $\sqrt{S}$ in the formula. This shall not apply to yachts masted before December, 1939.

(ii) *Mainsail Headboard:* If the effective horizontal extension of headboard of a Bermuda mainsail exceeds 3 per cent of the length of the boom, 30 times the excess shall be added to the boom, "*b*".

(iii) *Spinnaker Headboard:* If the greatest width of headboard of a spinnaker exceeds 5 per cent of the length of the spinnaker boom, 20 times the excess shall be added to the spinnaker boom.

(iv) *Boom:* If the maximum depth of the boom exceeds 4 per cent of its length, the excess shall be multiplied by the length of the spar and added to the total sail area.

(v) *Battens:* Battens, if fitted, shall divide the leach into approximately equal parts; they shall not exceed five in number. The maximum length of the longest batten shall not exceed 14 per cent of boom plus 1.5 feet if four or fewer battens fitted; or 12 per cent boom plus 1 foot if five battens fitted.

If any batten exceeds the above limit, twice the excess of each such batten shall be added **to** the length of the boom "*b*".

(vi) *Yawls and Ketches:* If the area of the mizzen sail of a yawl is less than 9 per cent or that of a ketch less than 18 per cent of the total sail area, the deficiency shall be added in computing S.A.

Prohibitions.—

(i) The spinnaker shall not have a foot stick, or more than one sheet, or any contrivance for extending the sail to other than a three-cornered shape.

(ii) Rotating masts and double-luffed mainsails are prohibited.

(iii) Special light-weather mainsails shall not be allowed.

ALLOWANCES

Rig Allowance.—

(i)

$$\sqrt{S} =$$

Bermudian Cutter	100%	$\sqrt{SA}$
Bermudian Yawl	98%	$\sqrt{SA}$
Bermudian or Wishbone Schooner and Gaff Cutter ..	96%	$\sqrt{SA}$
Bermudian or Wishbone Ketch and Gaff Yawl	94%	$\sqrt{SA}$
Wishbone Schooner on which no staysail is set above the wishbone	94%	$\sqrt{SA}$
Gaff Schooner	92%	$\sqrt{SA}$
Gaff Ketch	90%	$\sqrt{SA}$

(ii) *Rig:* The denomination of the rig, whether Bermuda or Gaff, shall be determined by the type of the mainsail.

(iii) *Schooners:* A Schooner in which the foreside of the main mast at the deck is further forward than 55 per cent of the water line length from the fore-end of the W.L., shall receive the rig allowance of a yawl.

Mizzen Staysails.—A deduction of 1 per cent of measured rating (M.R.) will be made in the case of a yawl or ketch if the owner declares, when applying for a Rating Certificate, that the yacht will not carry a mizzen staysail.

Light Alloy Masts.—An addition to rating of $1\frac{1}{2}$ per cent of MR will be made if the yacht has a mast of light alloy.

Bowsprit Allowance.—Jb = Length of bowsprit from outer side of stem to forward end of J, as defined in Rule 17 (i).

Bowsprit allowance = .07 (10Jb − J), to be deducted from J if positive.

This deduction shall not be taken into account in calculating the maximum sizes of head-sails and spinnaker which can be carried without penalty. Any penalty shall be added to J after bowsprit allowance has been applied.

Appendix 3

INTERNATIONAL CRUISER-RACER RULE
SAIL MEASUREMENT

Sail Area—"S".—The sail area is to be measured as laid down in "Instructions to measurers". The area so ascertained is to be multiplied by the rig factor (Appendix C) and entered in the formula as "S". The fore triangle is to be taken as 100 per cent. The distance between the foremost point of the base of the fore triangle and a perpendicular dropped from the clew of any headsail, when new (except spinnaker), is not to exceed 150 per cent of the length of the base of the fore triangle. Double luffed sails and similar contrivances are prohibited.

Two mainsails shall not be hoisted at any one time and not more than one spinnaker shall be broken out or hoisted if set without stops.

No sail shall be set unless its area is included in S.

Black bands at least one inch in width are to be used on spars. The inner edge of the black band shall indicate the limit to which the sail may be stretched. In the case of the head this is the upper inner edge of the cringle or upper edge of the headboard; in the case of the tack the upper side of the boom. In the case of the clew the after inner edge of the clew cringle. Chocks or stops are to be fitted so that the sails cannot be stretched beyond the inner edge of the black bands.

Maximum Height of Sail Plan.—The maximum height of sail plan allowed, measured from the top of the covering board at the side along the mast, shall be 1.65 class rating + 1.6 metre.

If any yacht should have a higher sail plan than aforesaid, the difference shall be multiplied by 3 and added to "M" which is the distance between the black bands on the mast. If any yacht should have a lower sail plan than the maximum, the difference shall be divided by 2 and deducted from "M".

If any yacht should have more than one mast and the height is less than 92 per cent of the maximum height, no further allowance is given. The allowance will in no case apply to more than one mast.

Should the top of the covering board at the point of measurement be higher than a straight line from the freeboard height at the forward girth station to the freeboard height at the aft girth station, then the height of the sail plan shall be measured from a point on this line abreast the mast and not from the top of the covering board.

Battens.—The number of the battens allowed in all yachts shall not exceed four in classes up to 9 METRES, and five in classes above 9 METRES and, if fitted, shall each be spaced within 9 inches above or below the respective points on the leech of the sail that divide the leech into five or six equal parts.

The maximum length of the longest batten shall not exceed 14 per cent of the length of the boom (mast to black band) plus .457 metre (1.5 feet).

Maximum height of fore triangle and limit to size of foresails.—The maximum height of the fore triangle for all classes is not to exceed, without penalty, 80 per cent of the allowed height of the sail plan. Should the height exceed the above limit then one-half of the excess is to be added to the actual dimension for computing the height of the fore triangle (I) for measurement purposes. The base of the fore triangle is not to exceed $.55 \times \sqrt{S}$.

The luff rope of headsails is to be a steel wire, except in the case of storm sails, of which the area is less than 75 per cent of the total area of the fore triangle, which may have a luff rope of hemp or manilla. The distance between the foremost point of the base of the fore triangle and a perpendicular dropped from the clew of any headsail (except spinnakers) is not to exceed 150 per cent of the length of the base of the fore triangle. Headsails may be changed at will and the replacing sail may be fully set and trimmed before the sail it replaces is taken in.

Spinnakers.—The halyards, where attached to the mast, may be .15 metre above the forestay and .05 metre out from the mast.

The luff and leech ropes to be a continuous wire rope of uniform thickness not less than .002 metre diameter.

The maximum length of the luff or leech of any spinnaker is not to exceed $.95 \sqrt{I^2 + J^2}$.

The foot and/or the widest part of the sail is not to exceed 180 per cent of the base of the fore triangle. Any spinnaker in which the widest part exceeds 150 per cent of the base of the fore triangle must be symmetrical about a line joining the head with the centre of the foot, and the width of the sail at half the distance between the head and the centre of straight lines joining the tack and clew must not be less than 75 per cent of the width between tack and clew.

No sleeves or other extensions are allowed.

Only two spinnakers are allowed to be on board when racing.

The spinnaker boom is not to exceed the length of the base of the fore triangle measured in the position of greatest extension from the mast to the inner edge of eye of tack fitting. The spinnaker boom must be carried and the spinnaker never used without a boom except during the operation of gybing.

Headboards.—The headboard of the mainsail is not to exceed 3 per cent of the measured length of the boom (mast to black band).

Masts.—The main mast to have a minimum diameter at half the height from the deck to the jib halyards, as follows:—

| | | | | | | Diameter | |
Class						Metres	Feet
7 METRE	..	..	..	..	..	.146	.478
8 METRE	..	..	..	..	..	.160	.525
9 METRE	..	..	..	..	..	.183	.600
10.5 METRE	..	..	..	..	..	.230	.750
12 METRE	..	..	..	..	..	.250	.820

The diameters may be reduced by 5 per cent at the deck, 20 per cent at the jib halyards and 50 per cent at the highest point of measurement, with a fair rounding taper from deck to top. The shell thickness at any cross-section shall be uniform, excepting at after edge, where it may be thickened to take track fastenings.

A wooden mast shall be solid from the step to 0·3 metre (1 foot) above the deck, excepting that for passing halyards a hole is permitted, the area of which shall be added to the sectional area of this part.

The athwartships diameter of masts which are not round may be reduced by not more than 10 per cent. If the athwartships diameter is reduced as permitted, the fore and aft diameter may be increased by not more than 35 per cent of the actual athwartships diameter. The sectional area of such masts shall not be less than the area of the circles of the rule diameters.

If the mast is solid it may be reduced in diameter by 8 per cent.

Appendix 4

INTERNATIONAL 5.5 METRE CLASS

SAIL MEASUREMENT

Limits of Actual Sail Areas.—

    Maximum "S", 29 sq. metres (312 sq. ft.).

    Minimum "S", 26.50 sq. metres (285 sq. ft.).

Sail Area.—Is the actual measured area of the mainsail, plus that of the largest headsail. No headsail shall be less than 80 per cent of the fore-triangle for measurement purposes.

If any device of any material is used which increases the area of the sail beyond its area measured in accordance with these rules, this additional area is to be added to the area of the sail for rule purposes.

Double luffed sails are prohibited.

Measurement of Area of Head Sail.—The maximum height of sail plan is 11.1 metres (36.4 ft.). It is to be measured from the deck at covering board level to the underside of upper black band.

The maximum height of the fore triangle is 8.88 metres (29.11 ft.) above the level of the covering board.

The base of the fore triangle is not to exceed 50 per cent of the square root of the area of the sail plan.

The area of the largest headsail is half the length of the luff multiplied by a perpendicular from the luff rope to the clew when hauled hand tight and when folded double on the luff. The luff ropes to be of wire rope. No jib shall have a club foot, battens, headboard, or yard and the shape shall be triangular.

Measurement of Area of Mainsail.—The area of the main triangle is the luff multiplied by the boom divided by 2.

The luff is measured from top of black band, below which the top of boom cannot be lowered, to the bottom of black band above which the top of head board cannot be hoisted. Stops are to be fitted at these positions.

The boom is measured from the inner edge of black band at boom end along the top of boom to the after side of the mast excluding the track or jackstay; but if there is a groove in the mast for the sail, to the foreside of the groove. The breadth of mainsail at half of lengths of luff and leech must never exceed 60 per cent of length of boom, and three-quarters of those lengths is not to exceed 35 per cent.

Headboard.—No dimension shall exceed 12 centimetres (4.72 in.).

Battens.—Four are allowed equally spaced. The top batten shall not exceed 75 centimetres (2.46 ft.) and the others shall not exceed 1 metre (3.28 ft.).

Spinnaker.—The halyards where attached to the mast may be 10 centimetres (3.9 in.) above forestay and 3 centimetres (1.18 in.) out from mast.

The luff and leech ropes are to be continuous wire ropes of uniform thickness and equal length. The maximum lengths of luff or leech are not to exceed the height of the fore triangle.

The breadth of half the foot, when folded tack to clew, is not to exceed the base of the fore triangle multiplied by 1.25.

When the spinnaker is folded tack to clew the width at a point half-way down the periphery of the fold to a point half-way down the leech shall not be less than 75 per cent of the length from the clew to the end of the centre line.

Only two spinnakers are allowed to be on board when racing.

Spinnaker Boom.—Is not to exceed the length of the base of fore triangle and is to be measured in the position of greatest extension from the mast to the inner edge of eye of tack fitting.

Mast—Wood or Metal.—The diameter at half the height from the deck to jib halyards is not to be less than 11.5 centimetres (4.52 in.). The diameters may be reduced by 5 per cent at the deck, by 50 per cent at top and by 20 per cent at jib halyards.

The athwartship diameter of masts which are not round may be reduced up to 10 per cent and the fore and aft diameter may be increased by $3\frac{1}{2}$ times the amount by which the athwartship diameter is reduced. The sectional area of such masts shall not be less than the area of circles of the rule diameters. Permanently bent or rotating masts, or mechanically bent booms are not allowed.

The minimum weight of masts is to be 35 kilogrammes (77 lb.) with all fixed fittings. The centre of gravity of mast shall not be lower than 38 per cent of its height above covering board level.

Masts must not be stepped on deck.

Boom.—The maximum height to top of the black band marking the lowest position of boom for measurement of sail area is 85 centimetres (2.79 ft.) above the covering board level. Boom must not be deeper than 15.2 centimetres (6 in.) or less than 3.8 centimetres (1.5 in.) wide.

INDEX